GREAT

CORAL
REEFS

GREAT
CORAL
REEFS

JOSEPH WALLACE

PHOTOGRAPHS BY WATERHOUSE

MALLARD PRESS

An imprint of BDD Promotional Book Company, Inc.
666 Fifth Avenue
New York, New York 10103

A FRIEDMAN GROUP BOOK

Published by MALLARD PRESS
An imprint of BDD Promotional Book Company, Inc.
666 Fifth Avenue
New York, New York 10103

Mallard Press and its accompanying design and logo are trademarks of BDD
Promotional Book Company, Inc.

ISBN 0-7924-5747-1

GREAT CORAL REEFS
was prepared and produced by
Michael Friedman Publishing Group, Inc.
15 West 26th Street
New York, New York 10010

Editor: Dana Rosen
Art Director: Jeff Batzli
Designer: Susan Livingston
Photography Researcher: Daniella Jo Nilva

Typeset by The Typecrafters Inc.
Color separations by United South Sea Graphic Art Co., Ltd.
Printed and bound in Hong Kong by Leefung-Asco Printers Ltd.

DEDICATION

For Jonathan and Richard, from Stony Beach
to the world's most beautiful reefs.

TABLE OF CONTENTS

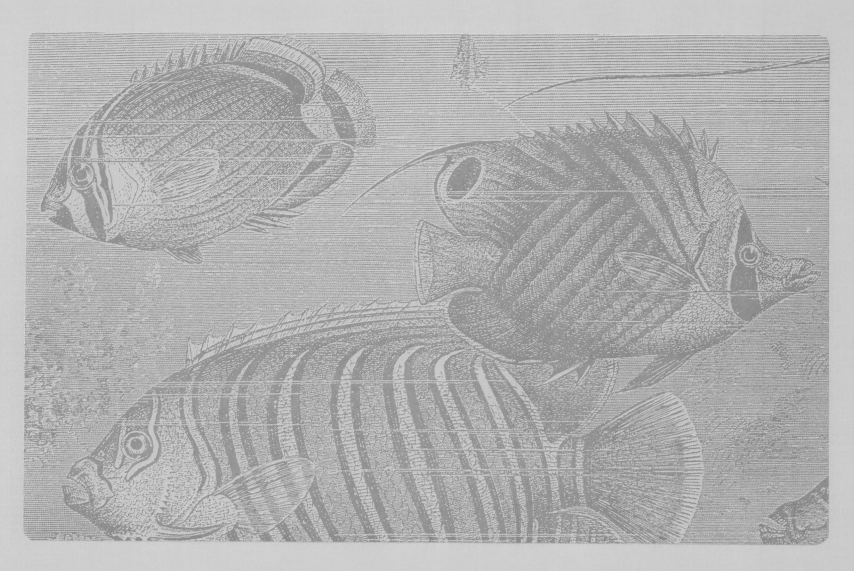

CHAPTER ONE:

The Making of a Coral Reef

First, you plant your coral. Then, you fertilize it, provide it with plenty of sunlight and water, and give it time. Soon you'll begin to see it sprout, spread, and bloom: your gorgeous coral garden, flowering in shades of orange, green, purple, and yellow. The garden will attract beautiful fish, darting among the coral like butterflies, as well as other wildlife. You couldn't ask for a more stunning show from your tulips or roses.

Although such a coral garden sounds very appealing, it's not really possible to grow a coral reef as you would a flower garden in your backyard.

In fact, the ecology of a reef is so complicated that even public aquariums, with their enormous tanks and high-technology filtration systems, have met with repeated failure in trying to establish a healthy "captive" reef.

But the garden analogy—impossible to ignore from the moment you first glimpse the reef—is still an apt one. Like plants, corals do require sunlight, clean water, and fertilizer, in the form of food. Like plants, they tend to stay in one place. Some of them even look like ferns, others like spiny cacti, still others like tall, many-branched trees.

But corals aren't plants, they're animals—some of the most remarkable animals found on earth. Along with the plants, fish, reptiles, and other living things that share the reef ecosystem with them, they've got a fascinating story to tell.

Perhaps you have just returned from diving on Australia's Great Barrier Reef. Or maybe you are planning a quick trip to the reefs that fringe the island of Bonaire, or you intend merely to spend a day on the reefs of the Florida Keys. Whether you have actually explored some of these reefs, or are just dreaming of your first visit, you'll better appreciate the beauty and complexity of the reef if you have a deeper understanding of how this extra-ordinary ecosystem evolved.

THE HISTORY OF CORAL REEFS

Reefs are among the most ancient life forms that still thrive on earth. Scientists think that the first corals, called rugose corals, evolved as long as 500 million years ago, during the middle Ordovician period, almost 300 million years before the dinosaurs appeared. In fact, although the first corals shared the oceans with early plants, as well as trilobites and other primitive invertebrate animals, they predate all land plants.

These original rugose corals survived for about 300 million years, finally becoming extinct about 200 million years ago. They were succeeded, however, by similar corals, called scleractinian corals, the first ancestors of today's coral reefs.

These scleractinian corals evolved in the warm, clear waters of the Tethys Sea, which then occupied an enormous area between the northern landmasses (which are now Europe and Asia) and the southern ones (which became Africa and the Indian subcontinent). Over the course of millions of years, the southern landmasses gradually drifted northward, shrinking the western edge of the Tethys Sea. As this occurred, the scleractinian corals were forced eastward, until they ended up in what is today the western Pacific.

Even now, millions of years later, it is evident that this area was the beneficiary of the Tethys Sea's coral abundance. Today, the islands, atolls, and coastal waters of the western Pacific boast more than five hundred species of coral—far more species than can be found anywhere else on earth.

The history of coral reefs since the first rugose corals has not been a steady, unbroken evolution toward more advanced and more spectacular animals. Instead, corals—along with all other marine organisms—have experienced times of extraordinary abundance, interspersed with times during which great extinctions have wiped out the vast majority of all the ocean's living creatures.

After their arrival, the first reefs prospered for 130 million years. Then came the first of three catastrophes, which mowed down the majority of all undersea animals and left only a few sickly reefs in existence. Scientists don't know what caused this extinction, but they suggest that it might have been the result of sudden changes in water temperature or depth.

For a full thirteen million years, the hardiest reefs hung on, surviving but not prospering. Finally, when conditions changed again, corals, sponges, algae, and other organisms once again spread across tropical seas. New

coral species evolved and others died out, but as a group, the corals became tremendously successful.

The second catastrophe struck about 225 million years ago, during the late Triassic period. Corals were not alone in suffering mass extinctions at this time: Scientists believe that *half* of the earth's taxonomic families became extinct in a remarkably brief period of time. Whatever the cause, coral reefs were almost completely wiped out. But some corals survived, and eventually the scleractinians, the corals that populated the Tethys Sea, emerged.

Then, about sixty-five million years ago, at the end of the Cretaceous period, the last and greatest extinction struck. This was the cataclysm that destroyed every dinosaur, every great marine reptile, every winged reptile, and countless other species. One-third of all families of marine organisms disappeared, including two-thirds of all corals.

Today, the debate still rages over what caused these catastrophic extinctions. Continental drift, for example, drained the shallow tropical seas, changed salt levels in the sea, created new currents, caused violent volcanic eruptions throughout the world, and carried landmasses into far colder climes than ever before. Any or all of these effects could have caused the wave of extinctions.

For the world's coral reefs, millions of years of abundance and diversity have alternated with eons spent fighting for survival.

Some scientists believe that a giant comet or asteroid—or a blizzard of them—may have struck the earth at this time. Such an event may have raised enormous clouds of dust, obscuring the sun and causing eons of unnaturally cold weather. Whatever the cause, most of the earth's living things were not able to adapt to these new conditions; but some scleractinian corals were able to survive and to thrive once again after the extinction passed. In the millions of years since the last extinction, scleractinian corals have again spread across the world's tropical seas.

Yet, despite their past successes in surviving enormous changes, the outlook for coral reefs may not be promising. The reefs are facing serious threats from human pollution and overfishing. In addition, during the sixty-five million years since the great extinction, the world's oceans have become steadily, although very slowly, colder. Tropical seas, the only ones warm enough to support coral reefs, are growing smaller. Today's reefs will have to adapt to these challenging conditions in order to survive in the future.

SO WHAT EXACTLY ARE CORALS?

Hungry Coral

Some scientists, pointing out that not enough zooplankton (corals' main food source) exist in some reef areas to support the vast number of hungry polyps, believe that zooxanthellae themselves may actually serve as a food source for corals. Even if this is the case, however, the corals clearly cannot depend entirely on the tiny plants. A coral polyp deprived of zooplankton will eventually expel its zooxanthellae and then die.

When you look at a coral reef, what you're seeing is a mass of limestone: the cementlike shells, many uninhabited, of countless coral animals. Even in living corals, the animals themselves, called polyps, tend to hide during the day. If you go diving at night, though, you'll see them: tiny (as small as one-quarter inch [1 cm], and rarely larger than six inches [15 cm]), soft-bodied creatures of great beauty and strangeness.

Coral polyps belong to the phylum Coelenterata and are related to jellyfish and sea anemones. Like those other coelenterates, polyps' simple bodies are basically cylindrical in shape and feature a single opening, surrounded by tentacles, which serves both to ingest prey and eliminate wastes.

For such basic creatures, corals and other coelenterates boast remarkable defense and prey-catching structures called nematocysts, which are located in the tentacles. Shaped like a tiny capsule, each nematocyst contains a minuscule barbed thread coiled like a spring. When the coral senses the presence of a potential meal (either by physical contact or through its chemical "senses"), the thread uncoils, bursts out of the nematocyst, buries itself in the victim, and injects a paralyzing poison. A few such stings are usually enough to subdue zooplankton, the tiny waterborne animals that the corals feed on. The coral's tentacles then pass the trapped, paralyzed plankton through the mouth opening to the stomach.

Their hunting technique is not the only unusual thing about the corals. If you take a look at a stand of staghorn coral, for example, you will think you're looking at thousands—or millions—of individual animals that joined together to form a colony. But what you are actually glimpsing is work that began with a single founding coral polyp. This founder replicated itself again and again, eventually making a colony of identical animals, all of which are also busily replicating themselves to form a vast colony: the coral reef.

If you once thought corals were plants, you were wrong—but not entirely so. Remarkably, all reef-building corals (as well as many other coelenterates) host millions of tiny one-celled plants, called zooxanthellae, within their tissues. The relationship between the corals and the zooxanthellae is a fascinating story of symbiosis.

The zooxanthellae benefit from the protection they receive, guarded by the polyps' hard coral skeletons and stinging darts. In their safe havens, they undergo the process of photosynthesis, converting water and carbon dioxide into carbohydrates, their food, and oxygen, a byproduct.

But that which is a byproduct to a plant can be essential to a coral. From the zooxanthellae, the polyps gain a steady supply of fresh oxygen to their tissues. In addition, some of the carbohydrates and other nutrients produced by the plants are actually used by the corals as food. This additional food and oxygen helps give the coral polyps the energy to produce their limestone skeletons—in other words, to build the coral reef itself.

(For more on the symbiotic relationship between coral polyps and zooxanthellae—and on other examples of symbiosis on the reef—see Chapter Three, page 66.)

These massive brain corals (right) seem about as vulnerable as a block of cement, but they contain thousands of fragile polyps.

HARD AND SOFT CORALS: A FASCINATING VARIETY

No one knows for sure how many different types of corals there are, but scientists have already identified thousands of different coral species. Most of them fall into one of two categories: hard or soft corals.

Hard corals, which include such well-known corals as the staghorns, elkhorns, and brain corals, are the building blocks of the reef. Most hard corals replicate constantly, and secrete limestone endlessly, forming the vast coral colonies that dominate the reef.

Like most hard corals, soft corals also occur in colonies, but the structures they build tend to be smaller and far more fragile. Unlike hard corals, many soft corals do not contain zooxanthellae, which require light to perform photosynthesis, in their tissues. Therefore, these soft corals are able to grow in deeper waters where light is not as available. And unlike hard corals, which anchor themselves permanently to a rock or to another patch of reef, some remarkable soft corals never lose the ability to move. These corals stretch the tissues in their bases in the direction they wish to travel and slowly—very slowly—edge their way along.

One major group of soft corals are the alcyonarian corals, found on Australia's Great Barrier Reef and other Pacific reefs. These feathery, vulnerable-looking corals seem at first to have no skeletons at all. But they actually contain tiny limestone crystals, called sclerites, within their tissues.

Another type of soft coral, more familiar than the alcyonarian corals to divers and snorkelers in the Caribbean, are the gorgonians. These include the gloriously beautiful sea fans and sea whips, which contain sclerites, but also boast a second interior skeleton made of a flexible material called gorgonin.

Many soft corals are extraordinarily beautiful and some are almost garish. Sea fans and other soft corals in gorgeous shades, such as yellow, orange, pink, and velvety purple, are familiar to snorkelers and divers. Interestingly, it is not usually the polyps that give these corals their color, but the sclerites within them.

WARM, CLEAR, SUNNY, SHALLOW: THE BEDROCK OF REEF DEVELOPMENT

Coral reefs require very specific environmental conditions in order to thrive. First, they need warm water, usually at temperatures not below seventy-three degrees Fahrenheit (23°C)—although a few reefs, such as those found in the Florida Keys, can survive at temperatures as low as sixty-four degrees Fahrenheit (18°C). Therefore, coral reefs are found only in tropical and sub-tropical seas, almost all of which fall within twenty-five degrees north and south of the equator. Individual corals can live in colder waters, but they do not form extensive reefs.

The second important requirement of coral reefs is light. The hard reef-building corals depend on the carbohydrates supplied by zooxanthellae to produce their limestone skeletons, and zooxanthellae need light to survive. Therefore, the deeper you go, the less reef building you will see. In many areas, the only noticeable corals below seventy feet (21 m) or so will be sea fans and other soft corals that do not contain zooxanthellae.

Not surprisingly, corals that depend on sunlight also require clear water. Sediment suspended in the water, such as that left by river runoff or pollution, will block the sun, shut down the zooxanthellae, and slow or halt the growth of the reef. Sediment that is not suspended, but that settles on the coral itself, is just as detrimental. This silt clogs and fouls the polyps' tentacles and mouths, making them unable to hunt or breathe.

Some corals are better able to withstand silt than others. For example, some *Platygyra* corals, better known as brain corals, produce large quantities of mucous when sediment levels are high. The mucous slides along the surface of the coral's skeleton and is borne away by the current, taking the sediment with it. But most coral colonies that are subjected to a steady supply of silt will not be able to survive, and they will soon become ghost towns. (For more information on threats to the reef, particularly those inflicted by human activity, see Chapter Five: "A World without Reefs?")

The Deeper You Go

It is known that coral reefs dwindle in size as ocean depth increases and available light diminishes. Remarkably, however, in certain areas, such as reefs in the Red Sea off the coast of Israel, the number of species of coral may actually increase as you descend.

Scientists believe that this anomaly exists because deeper waters are environmentally stable, encouraging species diversity, while shallow waters can suffer wide variations in temperature, salinity, and other factors that can limit reef growth.

Soft corals, such as this gaudy Red Sea gorgonian (above), are often found on deeper, darker areas of the reef.

In addition to warm water, light, and clear water, reef-building corals also require salt levels that are characteristic of the open ocean. If conditions change, for example if heavy rainfall leads to flash floods or excessive fresh-water runoff from nearby rivers, causing the overall salt-to-water ratio to decrease, coral colonies will die. The reverse also holds true: If an area hosting a reef suddenly undergoes a rise in salinity, most corals will soon begin to languish.

Last, corals can only thrive in areas of strong currents or high wave energy. The constant change of water serves several purposes: It tends to keep the coral habitat relatively free of silt or suspended sediment, to maintain steady, healthy salt levels, and to send a steady stream of zooplankton past the polyps' tentacles.

CORAL REPRODUCTION:
SEXUAL AND ASEXUAL OPTIONS

We have already discovered that a single coral polyp can replicate itself endlessly, forming new polyps that replicate themselves in turn. This process is called budding, a type of asexual reproduction. Because of this process, even a huge stand of elkhorn or staghorn coral can consist entirely of individual polyps that are all genetically identical. But this form of reproduction can be very risky. Budding confines a coral reef to a fixed spot, leaving it vulnerable to extinction if an environmental catastrophe hits the area in which it lives. In addition, a reef comprised of genetically identical polyps can more easily be destroyed by changing conditions than a reef whose corals replicate sexually and are genetically diverse; the sexually reproducing corals stand a chance of evolving at least some corals suited to the new conditions. Therefore, in order to help them colonize new areas and to maintain the survival of the species, many corals have also evolved a fascinating means of sexual reproduction.

The process of sexual reproduction begins with the gradual development of sperm and eggs in the polyps' sex organs, which are located in the mesenteries, the soft tissues that flank the stomach cavity. As much as six months before spawning, the eggs have already begun to develop; the sperm require less time to mature. In many species of coral, a single polyp contains both male and female sexual cells, although one polyp's sperm will not fertilize its own eggs. In other species, the sex of every polyp in a colony is either male or female. And, in a remarkable third option, other species of coral are sequentially hermaphroditic: The entire colony will start out as a single sex, then change sex en masse as time passes.

As they develop in the mesenteries, the eggs may become brightly hued with red, orange, or purple. The sperm take on the classic tadpole shape, which is most efficient for chasing down eggs: rounded, with a streamlined head followed by a strong, whiplike tail.

Eventually, both sperm and egg are mature—but still the corals don't spawn. What are they waiting for? In many cases, the answer is simple: the full moon. On the Great Barrier Reef and many other reefs, spawning almost always begins within a day or two following a full moon, usually in spring or summer.

During the days preceding spawning, the polyps gather their eggs or sperm just below their mouths. Then, as if on cue, dozens or more different species expel the masses into the current—to sink or swim. Seeing these great clouds of minuscule sex cells drifting like a multicolored snowfall is one of the most spectacular sights any diver could hope for.

Scientists debate why so many different species spawn at the same time. This habit would seem to lead to confusion, as sperm hopelessly try to fertilize eggs of another species. It is likely, however, that the sperm respond to some chemical signal given by eggs of their own species, and head only toward them. In fact, mass spawning may actually be to the corals' advantage. While predators lurk at spawning time, waiting for the sudden appearance of so much defenseless food, the simultaneous appearance of so many eggs and sperm at one time may overwhelm the appetites of even very hungry fish.

Other coral species spawn in a far less spectacular way. In these species, the eggs remain within the polyps' mesenteries, where they are fertilized by sperm carried by ocean currents. Only after the eggs hatch into spherical or elongated larvae, called planulae, are they ejected, usually one or two at a time, through the polyps' mouths.

At this point, these larvae develop just like the larvae that were hatched from eggs expelled during the mass spawning and fertilized in the water.

Long-Distance Travelers

While most coral spawnings enable coral species to colonize new areas near the spawning site, some species undertake far more dramatic journeys. In fact, the peripatetic habits of certain coral larvae are responsible for the formation of the Great Barrier Reef. According to Dr. Paul L. Jokiel, a researcher at the Hawaii Institute of Marine Biology, undersea volcanoes erupting 2,500 miles (4,000 km) east of Australia may provide the transportation for corals that end up on the Great Barrier Reef. In the volcano-riddled Tonga-Kermadec Trench, south of the island of Fiji, planulae hitch a ride on inch-long (2.5-cm-long) pieces of pumice, lava stones ejected from the trench's many volcanoes.

Vast numbers of pumice pebbles flow in the prevailing currents to the shallow waters off northeastern Australia, home of the Great Barrier Reef. During the journey, the coral larvae become full-grown polyps and then begin to replicate, often covering half of a pebble before arriving at the great reef. At this point, each tiny coral colony either anchors itself to the reef or sends out new larvae, which then attach themselves to the reef and begin forming new colonies.

Using cilia, tiny hairlike swimming structures, the planulae swim and drift amid the great mass of other planktonic animals. Countless numbers of them are eaten by waiting predators, including, without a doubt, some of the same coral animals that just spawned them.

Over the course of a few days—possibly even weeks—the planulae grow larger and begin swimming closer to the sea floor, in search of an appropriate place to anchor. Once they've found the right spot, they settle (few ever to move again). They then develop into adult polyps, forming a mouth and tentacles and extruding a limestone skeleton, thus beginning the process of forming a new coral colony.

CORAL GROWTH: THE TORTOISE OR THE HARE?

Count the Rings

Scientists have come up with several different ways to measure the age and growth rate of corals. Perhaps the most revealing way is reminiscent of the method researchers use to learn the age of a tree: counting the growth rings.

As they grow, corals deposit limestone skeletons. But the rate of deposition varies with the season, due to changes in water temperature, available sunlight, and other factors. As a result, if you cut into the skeleton of a coral colony, you'll see alternating dark and light bands, each characterizing a season or a year.

Count these bands, and you'll discover that some living colonies are hundreds of years old.

You could spend days—even weeks—watching a coral reef, and at the end you would swear that coral never grows. It would seem to be exactly the same size and shape at the end of your survey as it was at the beginning.

Quick-growing staghorn coral is almost always the most abundant and widespread coral seen on shallow, sunlit Caribbean reefs.

The problem with watching corals grow is how slowly the process takes place: Even watching a plant grow is more satisfying.

In general, *Acropora* (staghorn) corals grow the most quickly of all corals. Their branches may extend as much as four inches (10 cm) each year, and the base of the colony may spread as much as three to four square feet (.3 to .4 square m) a year. On the other end of the spectrum, the large, blocklike *Montastrea* corals may grow as little as a quarter of a centimeter a year.

The growth of the Caribbean species *Montastrea annularis* demonstrates the way corals can adjust to different conditions. In waters thirty-three feet (10 m) deep or shallower, this species tends to grow in huge, hemispheric colonies. Each year, the predominant growth of the colony is upward, toward the surface. In deeper water, however, the same species takes on a far flatter and broader form, in the shape of an enormous plate. In addition, the colony tends to grow outward, not upward. Scientists think that this unusual growth process is an adaptation to diminished light conditions; the broader and flatter the colony, the more precious sunlight it will catch.

DEATH OF THE CORALS

It should come as no surprise that pollution can kill a coral colony. You may even know that certain predators, notably the crown-of-thorns starfish, can lay waste to enormous, generations-old coral heads. (For further information on the threats to corals, see Chapter Five: "A World Without Reefs?")

But the next time you float above or amid a seemingly peaceful coral reef, keep in mind that you're actually witnessing a constant, unrelenting battle. It's a battle for survival in an ecosystem in which space is the most important determinant. As discussed before, the perfect coral environment is one with exactly the correct temperature, salinity, clarity, light, and current or wave action. Only very specialized areas suffice, and competition for these areas is intense.

A coral reef may seem like one of the sturdiest ecosystems on earth. These dead star and elkhorn corals, however, bear testimony to the disastrous effects of even slight changes in temperature, salinity, or other conditions.

The methods corals use to conquer other corals vary greatly. Some methods are simple: One coral can grow over another, eventually depriving it of space, light, and food. Other methods are more subtle. For example, a tall and fast-growing staghorn or elkhorn coral is able to cast shade on a slower-growing coral below. The zooxanthellae in the shaded coral aren't able to photosynthesize, and the coral becomes undernourished, under-oxygenated, and unable to produce enough limestone, causing it to languish or die.

But this example does not prove that fast-growing corals always have the advantage. On many Caribbean reefs, solitary, slow-growing corals (including the previously mentioned *Montastrea annularis*) are among the most common—and therefore most successful—of all corals. How do they survive against their faster-growing neighbors?

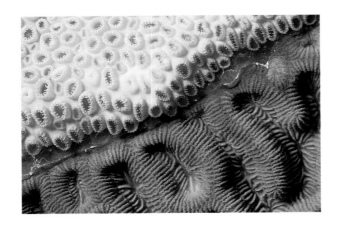

At first glance, these two coral species may appear to be peaceable neighbors. But in most cases, such close contact between different species results in a slow-motion war for territory, culminating in the death of one coral head.

Odd as it sounds, scientists have found that a coral's ability to succeed is correlated with its aggressiveness. Many corals, particularly the slow-growing species, have the ability to kill their adjacent neighbors. And the process is far quicker than you might imagine, given the tortoiselike pace of so much of a coral's life.

One researcher, placing two species of *Scolymia* corals next to each other in an aquarium, found that within only a few hours one of them had sent out "runners," which are filaments of stomach material that fastened onto the other coral and quickly digested the parts of it that were within reach. In contrast, when a larval *Scolymia* settles beside another individual of the same species, neither gets eaten; instead, the two merge and they form one large colony.

Many coral species have the ability to attack and digest neighboring corals. In one study of Caribbean reefs, researchers found that a hierarchy existed: A given coral species would always digest the corals below it in the hierarchy, and it would be digested by those above it. But coral battles are not always a matter of who can digest whom. Sometimes, a coral will turn its stinging cells on a neighbor; the poison contained in the cells may be potent enough to kill other corals.

The *Scolymia* corals are among the most aggressive of all corals. *Scolymia lacera*, for example, is capable of digesting any other species that happens to settle near it. Not surprisingly, this is a solitary species, rarely found anywhere near other corals.

FRINGES, BARRIERS, AND ATOLLS

Because his discoveries on the Galápagos Islands and his subsequent theories about evolution are so famous, we tend to forget how remarkable a scientist—and how intrepid a world traveler—Charles Darwin was. During his voyages on the *Beagle* and other ships, Darwin saw and recorded a countless number of previously unnoticed natural phenomena, ranging from discoveries of new species to the influence of the ocean currents on animal life.

Darwin did not neglect the spectacular handiwork of coral reefs. "We feel surprise when travelers tell us of the vast dimensions of the pyramids and other great ruins," he wrote in *The Voyage of the Beagle*, describing a visit to a coralline island in the Indian Ocean. "But how utterly insignificant are the greatest of these, when compared to the mountains of stone accumulated by the agency of various minute and tender animals!"

During the same voyage, Darwin developed a theory of coral-reef formation. All reefs, he decided, fell into one of three great classes: atolls, barrier reefs, and fringing reefs. Each of these classes was characterized by a specific shape and coral growth pattern, and each sprang from subtly different environments.

Today, some scientists have cut the number of reef types to two: coastal reefs, which includes both fringing and barrier reefs, and atolls. Others, however, have added several new subcategories, and now count patch reefs, platform reefs, and coral knolls as legitimate reef structures. The following descriptions should help you determine what type of reef you're diving on or floating over.

Barrier Reefs

Even the reef neophyte is familiar with the Great Barrier Reef, an unparalleled 1,200-mile-long (1,920-km-long) pinnacle of reef development. But a reef does not have to be that large to be considered a barrier reef; it just needs to fit certain categories, first devised by Charles Darwin and still used by scientists today.

From the air or from underwater, barrier reefs are one of the most spectacular natural structures found on earth.

Along the Eastern Coast

Anyone who has studied the location of the world's barrier reefs (not only the Great Barrier Reef, but the 200-mile [320-km] reef located in the Caribbean off Belize, and others), can instantly spot the same odd fact: Barrier reefs only seem to occur off the eastern coasts of landmasses. As discussed before, reefs grow only where the proper conditions occur, and one of the necessities is warm water. The world's oceans are in the grip of currents so vast that it's hard to see them from up close. But these currents tend to carry cold water along the western edges of the continents and warm water along the eastern edges. This discrepancy in temperature results in spectacular variances in the amount of coral growth between eastern and western coasts.

Barrier reefs, which fall into the larger category of coastal reefs, are long, wall-like structures that run parallel to the coastline of a landmass. They tend to lie more than half a mile (.8 km), and sometimes many miles, offshore, and to rise from deeper waters than most other reefs. Barrier reefs often protect the shoreline from strong currents and waves. The Great Barrier Reef, for example, has created a calm lagoon that reaches thirty miles (50 km) in width between the reef and the Australian coast.

Scientists continue to debate exactly how barrier and other coastal reefs develop. Darwin did not believe that these reefs anchor in water hundreds of feet deep (a near impossibility, given the zooxanthellae's crucial need for light), and then strive toward the surface. He asserted that the presence of barrier reefs is evidence that changes in either sea level or land level have occurred over the course of millions of years.

Most likely, a barrier reef starts developing in shallow water close to shore. As time passes, however, the nearby landmass settles (a process called subsidence), or the ocean rises (scientists have found that sea levels have fluctuated by hundreds of feet throughout history), and so the reef appears to have moved further from the shore. The change in depth occurs slowly enough that the living corals are able to grow toward the surface, staying close enough to the light-filled surface regions to survive. The result is a barrier reef, dozens or hundreds of feet tall, which seems to have sprouted in deep water, far from any land.

Both barrier and fringing reefs begin to develop in shallow water near the coast of a landmass, although sections of some barrier reefs may eventually form many miles from shore.

Fringing Reefs

Fringing reefs tend to occur in shallow, light-filled waters near shore. They may begin as just small patches of coral, but they eventually grow and join together, running parallel along the shoreline, sometimes even for miles. Fringing reefs may develop into barrier reefs if, over the course of thousands or millions of years, the sea level rises sufficiently to separate the reef from the coastline by many miles.

Geologists studying the origins of reefs can easily see the age difference between fringing and barrier reefs. They have discovered that a living barrier reef often sits atop thousands of feet of ancient coral, sometimes dating back twenty million years or more. In contrast, the structure of a fringing reef may extend only one hundred feet (30 m) beneath the surface, atop sand or preexisting rock outcroppings that the coral polyps first anchored themselves to.

As with barrier reefs, fringing reefs create a calm lagoon bordering the coast. This lagoon, which may be only yards wide, becomes virtually separated from the nearby ocean. It may become extremely warm and salty, overly acidic due to decomposing leaves or other organic matter, and filled with sediment that otherwise would have washed out to sea. In other words, the calm lagoon created by the reef is not a hospitable place for corals to grow.

Thank the Coral

Once the coral facing the calm lagoon created by a fringing reef dies, it gradually erodes. The end result of this erosion is sand — which explains why so many tropical lagoons and beaches near reefs are so luxuriantly sandy.

Therefore, if you stand on an island fringed by reefs, you'll probably find yourself looking largely at the skeletons of dead coral. All of the action is happening on the side facing the sea, where the water still features proper levels of light and the other factors so important to healthy coral. If you want to see a fringing reef in all its glory, head for the reef's ocean face.

Atolls

If you've only visited reefs in the Caribbean, then you might have no idea that atolls, spectacular coral islands, exist. Travel to the Pacific or the Indian Ocean, however, and you'll soon discover what others have already learned: No man-made structures, and few natural ones, can outdo an atoll for pure magnificence.

Charles Darwin, keeping in mind the changes in sea level that help transform a fringing reef into a barrier reef, correctly figured out how an atoll develops its characteristic ring- or horseshoe-shaped structure. The process begins with an oceanic volcano, which may be hundreds or thousands of feet tall, but whose cone is only partly exposed above sea level. At this time, the volcano may be fringed by coral—but nothing more.

As time passes, the sea level rises and the seabed subsides, and the volcanic cone begins to sink below the surface. Simultaneously, the fringing reef, desperately trying to stay in the life-giving sunlit shallows, battles the rising water levels by growing taller and thicker.

Finally, the volcano disappears from view. Now the fringing reef, which has grown enormously around the volcano's cone, has assumed the familiar circular shape of an atoll. Dry land takes more time to develop. Eventually

Naming Atolls

The Maldive Islands in the Indian Ocean are famous for the abundance of their atolls. In fact, the word "atoll" comes from the Maldivian word for this coral formation: "atholhu."

The characteristic circular shape of a coral atoll (right) provides a ghostly reminder of the long-drowned volcano that once stood on the site.

sand and other sediment collect on top of the tallest sections of the reef, forming islets arranged in a circular- or horseshoe-shaped ring. These islets eventually become large and sturdy enough to support plants and palm trees, nesting birds, and other wildlife.

The development of an atoll is a slow, painstaking process. Scientists studying Eniwetok Atoll in the South Pacific have uncovered an astounding 1,540 yards (1,400 m) of ancient reef below the living reef that grows today. They believe that the first polyps may have fastened to the original rock surrounding an extinct volcano as long as sixty million years ago.

Patch Reefs, Platform Reefs, and Coral Knolls

Not all reefs fall easily into the classic categories of atolls, barrier reefs, and fringing reefs. Sometimes smaller reefs develop separately from the large, familiar formations, requiring their own designations. The differences between patch reefs, platform reefs, and coral knolls are as follows:

- *Patch reefs* look like small coral hills. Rarely more than 220 yards (200 m) in diameter, they tend to occur in shallow water and often pop up in sandy lagoons.
- *Platform reefs* are larger versions of patch reefs, and they grow in comparatively deeper water. They're usually more than 330 yards (300 m) in diameter.
- *Coral knolls,* the smallest independent formations of the three, are tiny outcroppings that rarely reach 55 yards (50 m) in diameter.

Circular Patch Reefs

Although circular coral formations are usually atolls, which develop from sinking volcanoes, patch reefs may also develop the near-circular shape of an atoll. The process begins as a patch reef grows larger. Coral growth on the side of the reef with more wave action is substantially greater than on the calmer edge. As the reef expands, the dead coral on the calm edge dies and erodes, leaving a sandy patch in the quiet water. Eventually, the outside edge encloses a sandy lagoon, islands begin to form on top—and the patch reef has taken on all the characteristics of a volcanic atoll.

ZONATION: A CLOSE LOOK AT THE REEF ECOSYSTEM

It's easy to assume, as you float placidly above the glorious coral heads of an expansive reef, that the coral reef is an independent, self-sufficient ecosystem. But this is not true. In fact, scientists are still learning how the reef interacts with seemingly unrelated environments close by. Grassy flats, mangrove swamps, and sandy lagoons all contribute to the geography of the reef. Scientists seek to understand these interactions by dividing the reef and nearby areas into zones and defining the role that each zone plays.

Views from the air reveal that the coral reef ecosystem includes sandy flats and mangrove swamps, along with the reef itself.

Fringing Reef Zonation

In order to understand the zonation of a fringing reef, pretend you're standing on a shore looking out at a reef. The zone nearest to you, encompassing the shoreline and the lagoon, is called the *back-reef* zone.

The shoreline of an island fringed by reefs is often composed of crumbled reef rock or silt, and it frequently provides abundant habitat for mangroves, tropical trees that can form dense forests. Beyond the shore and mangrove forest, the *lagoon* is usually a flattish, sandy area of calm, almost stagnant, waters. The lagoon may be no more than a few feet in depth, and it is often discolored by algae and overgrown by turtle grass or other sea grasses. Feasting on the grasses are mollusks, urchins, and other creatures that can withstand the lagoon's high salinity and variable temperatures. In addition, the young of many fish find the grasses a source of both food and cover. But corals are virtually absent in the shallower waters of the lagoon.

Moving farther from shore, the waters gradually become deeper, and the first corals appear. Generally, these pioneers include only a smattering of coral species, most frequently brain corals and other hardy species. Some lagoons, though, host patch reefs, which contain a wider variety of corals—though nowhere near the abundance that occurs on the reef itself.

Beyond the lagoon lies the *back reef*, the rearmost section of the fringing reef. Here, although salinity and temperature levels of the water are still influenced by the stagnant lagoon, the corals also receive the revivifying effects of cool, nutrient- and oxygen-rich water brought over the reef by waves. As a result, the number and variety of corals on the back reef are far greater than anywhere else in the lagoon.

Atop the back reef lies the *reef-flat* zone, a wave-pounded stretch that may be only a few inches high—or may even be exposed during low tides. This area can only host a few small corals, along with algae and mollusks. The algae of the reef flat are called calcareous algae, and are an ancient, primitive life form. But even these unimpressive plants serve an important role on the coral reef: Like coral polyps, they draw calcium carbonate from the ocean and produce limestone, which helps to strengthen the structure of the reef.

On the open-ocean side of the reef flat lies the *reef-crest* zone, which bears the brunt of currents and wave action, and again rarely holds many corals. Only ten to seventeen feet (3 to 5 m) below the crest on the seaward reef slope is the *reef front* or *forereef*. Here, the waves are less powerful, and corals begin to appear in great numbers. On many reefs, this zone boasts vast forests of staghorn and elkhorn (*Acropora*) corals, as well as many other coral species and an abundance of fish and other reef life.

Lower on the forereef, in a less well-lit area, the staghorn and other reef-building corals are replaced by sea fans, gaudy soft corals, and other corals that can grow in darker environments. The familiar reef—the reef that we know so well from diving, snorkeling, or merely looking at pictures—has come to an end.

Spur and Groove

Some fringing reefs, including many in the Caribbean, possess variations on this basic zonation plan. Perhaps most important, the deeper forereef of these reefs includes a broad, flat area at about eleven yards (10 m) in depth. This terrace-like region, called the *buttress zone*, is bisected at right angles to the shoreline by large, deep channels caused by tidal surge. Scientists call these channels "spur and groove" topography.

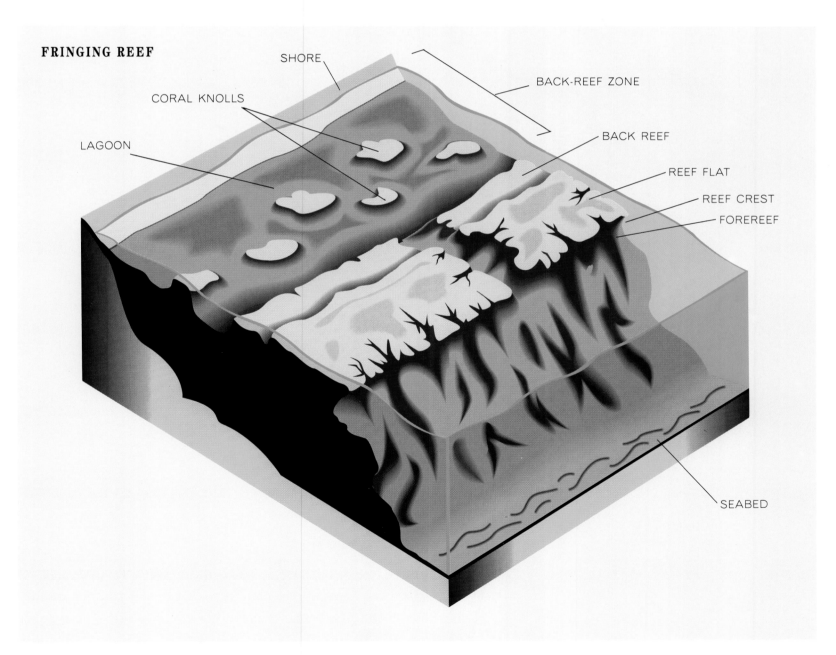

FRINGING REEF

SHORE

CORAL KNOLLS

LAGOON

BACK-REEF ZONE

BACK REEF

REEF FLAT

REEF CREST

FOREREEF

SEABED

Barrier Reef Zonation

The zonation of barrier reefs is similar to that found on fringing reefs, but it is not identical. Most important, barrier reefs lie much farther from the coast than fringing reefs. If you stand on shore and look out to sea, you might be able to spot the barrier reef lying far offshore. But you won't find a compact, easily defined back-reef zone with a sandy lagoon and fields of sea grass.

Instead, what lies between the reef and the shore can be called the *leeside* zone. This area, which can be as large as thirty miles (50 km) in width, contains conditions far more favorable to coral growth than does the back-reef zone of fringing reefs. Patch reefs and coral knolls can be abundant here, interspersed with sandy flats. On the Great Barrier Reef and other barrier reefs, some of the most exciting reef formations and interesting reef denizens can be found on the leeside.

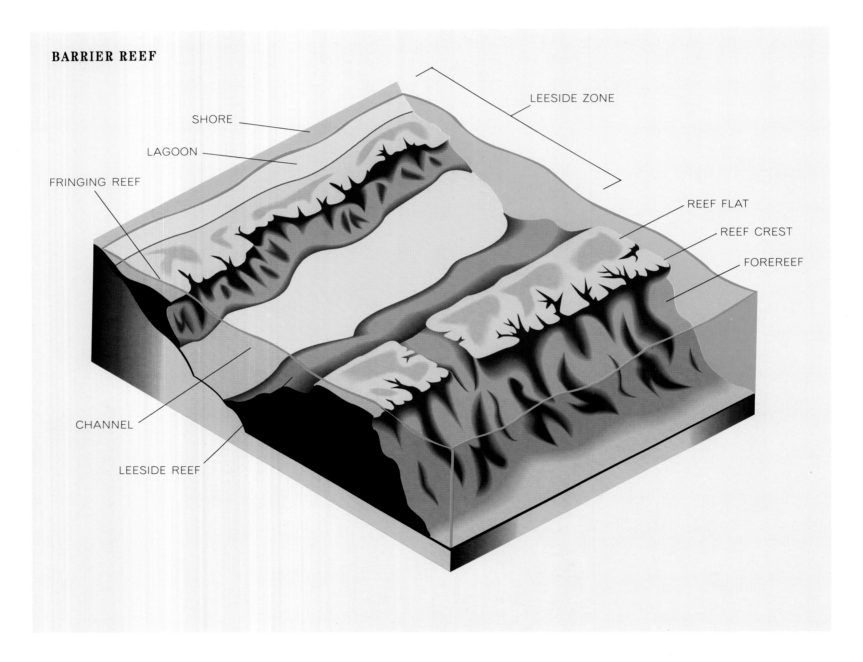

BARRIER REEF

SHORE

LAGOON

FRINGING REEF

CHANNEL

LEESIDE REEF

LEESIDE ZONE

REEF FLAT

REEF CREST

FOREREEF

Atoll Zonation

The pattern of zones that characterizes an atoll differs markedly from those in fringing- and barrier-reef formations. The zonation of an atoll is a virtually circular system, only one side of which bears the brunt of the prevailing winds and waves.

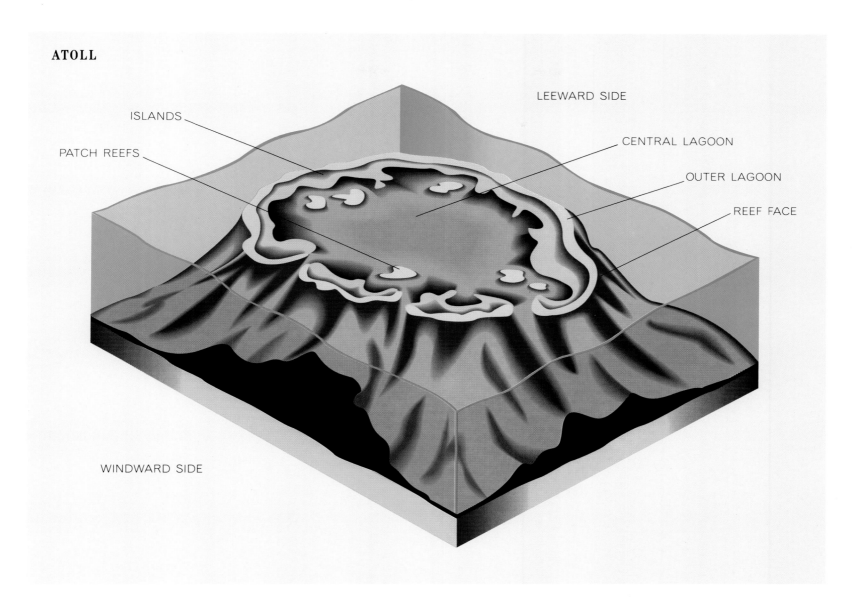

ATOLL

ISLANDS

PATCH REEFS

LEEWARD SIDE

CENTRAL LAGOON

OUTER LAGOON

REEF FACE

WINDWARD SIDE

Like the lagoons of fringing reefs, the atoll's *central lagoon* is often a calm, warm environment, rich in sea grasses and other organic matter, but not in corals. Sometimes, however, the outer reefs don't completely encircle the lagoon; the resulting currents can allow large patch reefs and coral knolls to grow.

On the outside of the atoll's patch reefs—but only on the leeward side, protected from the wind and waves—lies a second, smaller lagoon: the *outer lagoon*. This is another sandy zone, with similar life forms as those found in other lagoons.

On the leeward side of the atoll, the sloping *reef faces* are rich in corals. This dense growth is found both on the side facing the central lagoon and on the side facing the outer ocean—even if the two sides are separated by a substantial island.

The windward side is a bit different. Again, dense corals grow on the slope facing the calm central lagoon. Massive corals also grow on a reef flat between the inner and outer reef slopes; the reef flat is protected from intense wave activity by a ridge of dead coral, carved by the waves, that may rise three feet (1 m) out of the water during low tide.

The outer reef slopes on the windward side take a severe pounding from the waves. Therefore, shallower waters here tend to feature more coral rubble than living coral. As the slope descends, though, coral growth improves—but not to the abundance and variety found in slightly calmer parts of the atoll.

Unsuccessful Atolls

Take a look at a successful, thriving atoll, and you know you're witnessing a marvel of adaptation. But not every potential atoll becomes an actual one.

In fact, the world's oceans are filled with drowned volcanoes that never metamorphosed into atolls. Some remain submerged more than one mile (1.6 km) below the ocean surface, their fringing reefs never even beginning the struggle to stay close to the surface. Others struggled and failed, becoming decomposed coral banks.

What makes one atoll succeed, and another fail? No one yet knows for sure.

CHAPTER TWO:

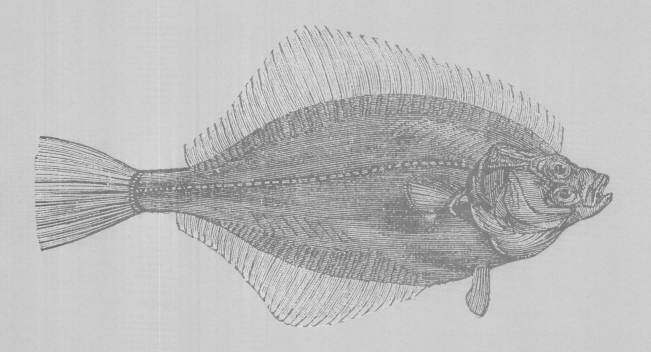

Creatures
of
the
Coral
Reef

U nless you're the world's coolest customer, on your first visit to a coral reef you'll find yourself stunned, overwhelmed, and dazzled. But it won't be the coral alone that takes your breath away. The most spectacular pageant on the reef belongs to the fish and the other creatures that make the reef environment one of the most varied and interesting on earth.

The reef environment is so rich that a snorkeler's single glance may encompass hundreds of individual fish from dozens of different species. A two-and-a-half-acre (1-ha) area of the Great Barrier Reef, for example, may contain two hundred fish species, along with hundreds of species of crustaceans, worms, sponges, and other creatures. Overall, the Great Barrier Reef hosts a stunning two thousand species of fish.

This extraordinary variety presents endless challenges to the new diver or snorkeler. Waterproof field guides to reef denizens are available in some areas; but if you don't know what to expect or what to look for, you're likely to return to the surface with little idea of what you've just seen.

Back on the boat and on shore after my first snorkeling trip on the reefs off the Florida Keys, I found myself arguing with my buddy—and also with myself. That large fish we saw lurking under a coral ledge was midnight blue with yellow fins, wasn't it? Or was it yellow, with blue fins? How about that snakelike creature protruding from a staghorn grove—that was a moray, right? Or was it a sand eel? Could it have been a sea snake?

Half an hour later I felt hopelessly lost. Everything I'd seen had become a blur of bright colors, varied shapes, and darting motions. I decided that I'd just have to keep visiting the reef until I could keep everything straight. But I also knew that there had to be a better way to learn about reef life.

The beauty and abundance of the reef and its inhabitants can be an overwhelming sight, particularly for the neophyte snorkeler or diver.

There is. For full enjoyment of the reef pageant, it helps to have some idea of the most common, most noticeable, and most exciting denizens of the reef before you go.

Having done a little research, I found that my enjoyment of the reef and its inhabitants was enormously enhanced. I began to notice more than color, shape, and movement. I knew that I hadn't merely glimpsed some large blue fish with a bulbous head—I'd seen a midnight parrotfish browsing on coral. Those two totally dissimilar fish that always seem to travel together weren't friends from different species—they were the male and female blue-head wrasse. And that snakelike form—it *was* a moray!

There's great pleasure to be gained from knowing what you're seeing. You will be equipped to appreciate the variety and beauty of life on the reef and better able to remember the fascinating things you saw after your dive is over. And you'll have more time for the really important arguments—such as whether the barracuda you all saw was actually twelve feet (4 m) or only eight feet (2 m) long.

THE ABC'S OF REEF LIFE

Although individual fish species tend to be restricted to specific oceans, a remarkable number of families—including such flashy ones as parrotfish, angelfish, and morays—are found on reefs worldwide. This section, therefore, will concentrate largely on family characteristics, instead of details about individual species.

Some types of young angelfish, as well as juveniles and adults of several other species, operate "cleaning stations." Remarkably, larger fish of many species congregate in an area staked out by one or more of the young angelfish. The juveniles then inspect the larger fish's bodies, even inside their mouths, picking off parasites.

Both sides benefit from this arrangement: The angelfish get a meal, and the larger fish get relief from itchy, and potentially harmful, parasites. Therefore, even a predator that would normally snap up an unwary young angelfish will leave those occupying a cleaning station at peace.

(For more on this joint activity, known as symbiosis, see Chapter Three, page 66.)

Angelfish

These large—some more than two feet (.6 m) in length—disc-shaped fish are so flat that, head-on, they can almost evade notice. View them broadside, though, and they're spectacular: green or blue with yellow highlights, trailing long, elegant fins.

If you see a fish that looks like a small angelfish, but is colored a drab brown with yellow vertical stripes, it is likely you're seeing a juvenile. Juvenile angelfish (as well as those of a few other families) often boast large, dark spots on their sides near their tail. These "false eyes" apparently evolved to scare away smaller predators, and to trick larger predators into attacking the angelfish's tail, instead of its head, allowing it to swim away comparatively unscathed.

Angelfish feed on algae and sponges. On reefs where such food is plentiful, the magnificent angelfish may be among the most common and noticeable of all reef species. Angelfish are also among the most curious fish on any reef. I've frequently encountered them swimming toward me, as if trying to get a better view. Above, a French angelfish.

Barracudas

There may not be a more spectacular fish commonly seen near coral reefs than the barracuda. With its streamlined bullet shape, its long jaw lined with daggerlike teeth, and its piercing dark eyes, the barracuda seems to radiate alertness and tension even when it's merely floating casually in the blue water above a reef.

Although barracudas don't usually spend much time among the coral, they use the populations of reef fish as a ready food source. It's not uncommon to see schools of small fish panicking, darting in all directions, and then to see a barracuda swimming away, a jack, grunt, or angelfish pinioned in its jaws. Above, a great barracuda.

Basslets

Many reef fish are so small that divers, dazzled by the spectacle of larger, more aggressive fish, tend to miss them entirely. But take a closer look at the pink fairy basslet pictured below and others of this elusive family, and you'll begin to appreciate the gemlike beauty of even the reef's smallest denizens. Oddly, basslets often swim upside-down under coral ledges, keeping their vulnerable bellies against the coral at all times.

Just Stay Calm

Like angelfish, barracudas can be extremely curious about humans. Without a doubt, it's a sobering experience to have a six-foot- (2-m-) long barracuda shadowing your every move, never taking its eyes off you, pausing in its surveillance only to swim within a foot (30 cm) of your mask and give you a long, cold stare. Luckily, barracudas won't bite unless cornered or threatened; they simply seem to be curious about visitors to their domain.

Blennies

Blennies are tiny fish, rarely more than three or four inches (8 or 10 cm) in length, which live on the reef itself. Like this seaweed blenny at left, these small fish dart out of nooks to chase away anything they think has invaded their territory. At least one species, the coral blenny, actually mimics the shape and coloration of its coral home.

Boxfish

If ever a family of fish had a perfectly descriptive name, it's the boxfish. Virtually rectangular, with small waving fins and bulbous eyes, these ungainly fish swim as if they're struggling against a strong current—even when they're actually floating in calm water.

Despite their slow, awkward movements, the boxfish have little to fear from most predators. In fact, they've got several lines of defense: the network of hard, bony plates that gives them their odd shape; strategically placed horns (which give some species the common name of "cowfish") that discourage attack; and—as if those weren't enough—the ability to secrete a deadly poison through their skin. Below, a honeycomb cowfish.

Brittle Stars

These limber creatures, pictured at left, resemble their better-known cousins, the sea stars (also known as starfish). But though both are echinoderms (as are sea urchins and sea cucumbers), they're actually only distantly related. If you see an animal with a small central disk, and remarkably long, thin arms, sometimes as much as a foot (30 cm) in length, you've found a brittle star.

To anyone used to the stolid, nearly immobile appearance of sea stars, the extraordinary mobility and speed of brittle stars can be shocking. Almost as soon as you've spotted it, you'll see it moving away, arm-over-arm, at what looks like fifty miles (80 km) an hour.

Butterflyfish

Resembling pint-sized versions of the angelfish, to which they are, in fact, closely related, butterflyfish are among the most graceful and prominent fish on almost every reef on earth. Rarely reaching a size greater than eight inches (20 cm), butterflyfish are usually garbed in yellow, gray, and black. They often patrol the reef in pairs, pausing only to search the coral for the tiny invertebrate animals that make up their diet. At right, two lemon butterflyfish.

Cardinalfish

Tiny nocturnal fish, cardinalfish have an irridescent pink coloration that makes them resemble small, fiery darts. Several species, including the flame-fish, have huge, black eyes oddly bisected crosswise with white stripes. Above, a gold-bellied cardinalfish.

Damselfish

Seeming to be in a constant hurry—and in a constant state of annoyance—damselfish may be the reef's most fearless inhabitants, despite their harmless appearance and diminutive size of less than six inches (15 cm). They are often seen darting out of crannies and attempting to chase away a diver floating peacefully among the coral heads.

For many new visitors to the coral reef, the sergeant major, a black-and-white striped member of the damselfish family, pictured at right, is one of the most easily identified fish. It is extremely common and easily seen. The young, in particular, travel in large schools and are often seen milling about above the reef and around moored boats.

Drums

Little known and bizarrely shaped, drums are strongly striped, knife-shaped fish, native to Caribbean reefs and largely nocturnal. Go diving or snorkeling early in the morning or just before dusk, and you may be lucky enough to spot one, most likely a spotted drum, hiding deep in a coral nook. Go night diving (more on the spectacular transformation of the reef at night in Chapter Three, page 56), and you'll be more likely to see drums swimming freely.

Drums are not named for their shape. Rather, they are comparatively noisy fish and get their name from the croaking, drumlike sounds that they make. At right, a spotted drum.

Feather Stars

Another relative of sea stars, feather stars are native to Indo-Pacific reefs and may be the most gorgeous of all echinoderms. Instead of the handful of arms found on most sea stars and brittle stars, feather stars, or crinoids, may have as many as two hundred feathery, plumelike arms, which may be crimson, lemon yellow, or even deepest purple in color. At night, and sometimes during the day, feather stars extend their arms from a coral cranny, trying to catch tiny planktonic animals. A feather star with a sea star is shown at left.

Filefish

These odd, bony fish, equipped with piglike snouts and tall, poisonous spines sprouting from their foreheads, would seem to be among the reef's most noticeable inhabitants. But filefish, which can range up to about three feet (1 m) in length, are masters of disguise. They tend to drift in the current, head down, appearing like nothing more than a bit of tidal flotsam. You may have to glance at a filefish two or three times before you realize that you're looking at a fish.

The largest Caribbean filefish, the scrawled filefish, is the most garishly decorated. Its tan body is covered in electric-blue dots and dashes, interspersed with black spots. Yet, this seemingly gaudy array quickly becomes indistinguishable from the background of the reef. It doesn't matter how brightly colored the scrawled filefish is in photographs or guidebooks—it's perfectly suited to its native environment. At left, a leatherback filefish.

Chameleon Fish

Many fish, including groupers and barracudas, have the ability to change color—sometimes dramatically. The peacock flounder, for example, will sometimes appear nearly white so that it can blend in with a sandy bottom; at other times, it will become dark gray-brown with peacock-blue spots and seem to disappear on the rocky sea floor.

Flounders

In general, flounders are far less common on the reef than they are on the sea floor. After all, rocky coral crags aren't the ideal home for flatfish. But in the grassy, sandy shallows that so often border fringing and barrier reefs and that form the central lagoon floor of atolls, the alert visitor may often spot a flounder, well camouflaged and half-hidden beneath the sand. Below, a spotted peacock flounder.

Killer Clams

It is a common fable, left over from B-movies and TV melodramas, that giant clams can close suddenly, trapping unwary divers far below the surface, and that the largest clams actually eat divers, leaving only a clean-picked skeleton behind.

Fortunately, these legends of murderous clams are indeed fables. You couldn't fit your foot into a giant clam if you tried. And even if you could, you'd have to work hard to get it lodged there.

Giant Clam

This common resident of Indo-Pacific reefs, pictured above, has more in common with coral than a large size (it is sometimes more than three feet [1 m] across) and staying power. In its gaudy purple-and-green mantle, the clam harbors a population of zooxanthellae, the tiny algae that also help many reef-building corals thrive. As they do for the corals, the zooxanthellae provide oxygen and food for the clam, while obtaining a safe place to live.

Goatfish

The design of goatfish, with their flat bellies and chins equipped with long, slender barbels, makes them effective bottom-feeding fish. Some goatfish also have the ability to change color more spectacularly than flounders and most other fish. The spotted goatfish, for example, can range from pale yellow to deep pink, depending on the color of the background.

Goatfish are among the most charming of all reef fish. There's something irresistibly endearing about the way they trail behind other bottom-feeding fish, inoffensively rooting through disturbed sand with their sensitive barbels. They look like shy street sweepers, bound by their duty but anxious to stay out of the way. At right, yellow goatfish.

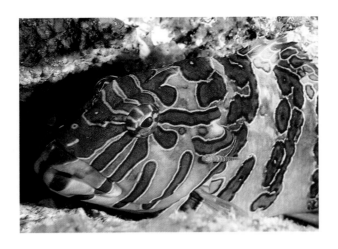

Gobies

Tiny fish, rarely more than two inches (5 cm) in length, gobies are usually painted in delicate blues, greens, and yellows. The strongly marked stripes that run along the sides of many species apparently serve to attract larger fish to the gobies' cleaning stations, where they eat parasites off these larger fish. One species, the cleaning goby, has even been named for this remarkable habit. The goby at left is cleaning a clown hawkfish.

Groupers

Groupers are a highly prized food fish; if you spot any large individuals, chances are you're on a comparatively undisturbed reef. When they get the chance to grow up, groupers can be awe-inspiring fish, with enormous, slablike bodies and heavy jaws. The jewfish, for example, can grow to be eight feet (2.4 m) in length, and weigh more than seven hundred pounds (315 kg). Yet, most groupers are shy and retiring, keeping to dark caves in the reef. Look for them close to the reef floor. Above, a tiger grouper.

Grunts

On any Caribbean reef, one of the most noticeable fish is the elegant blue-striped grunt, pictured at left, with its bright-blue racing stripes on a lemony background. But this fish is only one of many species of grunts commonly seen in schools on Caribbean reefs. Most are medium-sized fish that are rarely over two feet (.6 cm) in length, clothed in yellows, blues, and shades of gray. They're named for the loud grunting sounds they make, particularly when hooked.

Jacks

Sometimes you'll be swimming on the reef, perhaps watching a gorgeous damselfish or hulking parrotfish, when you'll suddenly feel as if a crowd is speeding past. You'll glance up and have the pleasure of watching a school of jacks, spectacularly streamlined, silver-and-blue fish that sometimes briefly grace the reef. Jacks use their extraordinary power and agility to hunt. Their strategy is to panic schools of reef fish, and then grab their prey and speed off into the open ocean. At left, purse-eyed scad.

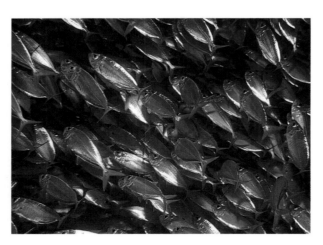

Transsexual fish

Perhaps the strangest fact about groupers is the way they grow up. At first, all sexually mature groupers are female. Then, as they grow older, they begin to change sex. For a time, some species will simultaneously possess fully working male and female sex organs (though they cannot impregnate themselves). Then, every grouper completes the transition and becomes male.

Morays

Are any reef inhabitants better known—or treated with more respect—than the morays? Only the great barracuda presents a more fearsome profile; but the morays have a disturbing snakelike form in addition to their heavy jaws and needlelike teeth.

Yet, morays, which tend to be shy and nocturnal, bite divers only when they feel threatened or cornered. Divers should not fear the moray, but should refrain from sticking their hands (or any other body parts) out of sight into coral nooks and crannies where morays may be hiding. Above, a green moray.

Needlefish

The redfin needlefish, pictured at right, is one of the most common of all Caribbean reef inhabitants. But it's extremely easy to miss. Needlefish, with their flattened backs, are ideally designed for life at the ocean surface, and most human visitors to the reef tend to look downward. But spy a needlefish, get a good look at its thin, tooth-filled mouth and its agile, darting movements, and you'll know you're glimpsing a powerful predator.

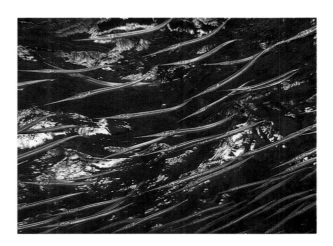

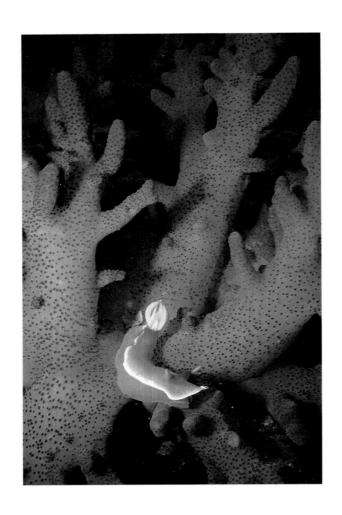

Nudibranchs

These astounding creatures are better known as sea slugs, which may be the most inappropriate name ever given to a reef animal. Shell-less relatives of the snails, the rainbow-hued nudibranchs (at left, a chromodoris nudibranch) are among the most spectacular and bizarre of all marine creatures.

Nudibranchs have a retiring nature and their habits are frequently nocturnal. But, though they're rarely glimpsed, nudibranchs are among the most diverse of all marine animals. Some scientists estimate that the world's oceans harbor five thousand different species, perhaps half of which have yet to be discovered.

Many nudibranchs boast extraordinary fringed gills, which twirl and spin as the animals make their dancing progress across the reef. Perhaps the most spectacular of all is the breathtaking Spanish dancer, crimson, pink, and white and twelve inches (30 cm) long.

Nudibranchs are so soft, so slow-moving, and often so brightly colored that they would seem to be prime bait for any passing predator. But that's far from the case, because most nudibranchs are highly poisonous. Amazingly, some "steal" the stinging cells from the corals they feed on, storing the cells in spines that run along their backs. Other nudibranchs have a different, but equally effective, defense system: They can release sulphuric acid or toxic slime upon attack. So, in fact, nudibranchs' bright colors actually serve as warning flags, announcing that the predator will regret eating them.

Don't Touch

It should go without saying that you shouldn't touch or handle any reef animals, but this is particularly true of octopuses. That lesson has been learned in the most tragic way by people who picked up the small, seemingly inoffensive blue-ringed octopus, native to the Great Barrier Reef region. This octopus is one of the world's most venomous animals, and several people have died after handling one.

Octopuses

Rarely seen, but undoubtedly more common than they seem, octopuses may be the reef's most entertaining inhabitants. With their large, intelligent eyes, their ability to change color dramatically from light to dark, and their waddling gait, octopuses are animals brimming with personality. Most octopuses are nocturnal. Look for them early or late in the day in dark crevices of the reef, where they spend the daylight hours. Above, a common reef octopus.

Parrotfish

Parrotfish are named for their oddly fused teeth, which, in fact, do resemble a parrot's beak. These common fish are large, with some species extending three to four feet (1 to 1.2 m) in length. They are also colorful (the midnight parrotfish is deepest blue, with green teeth) and tame, usually paying little attention to divers and snorkelers.

Parrotfish use their bizarre beaks to graze algae from dead patches of coral, actually breaking pieces off as they feed. If you swim quietly and hold your breath, you may be able to hear the crunching sounds they make as they convert the hard coral into fine sand.

Some parrotfish have a unique way of bedding down for the night. They'll find a cranny in the coral, settle inside it, and then envelop themselves in a shroud of mucous. Scientists think the mucous may be distasteful to potential predators, keeping them from attacking the sleeping parrotfish. Below, a rainbow parrotfish.

Puffers

These are the familiar—but no less remarkable—fish that have the ability to quickly ingest large quantities of water, puffing themselves up to three times their normal size in order to intimidate a potential predator. As if this wasn't enough of a defense, some types of puffers, known as porcupinefish and burrfish, are covered with sharp spines. Puffers tend to be slow-moving, almost awkward fish; due to their other defenses, they've never had to evolve speed or agility. At right, a white-spotted puffer.

Rays

It is a spectacular experience to glimpse a giant manta ray or eagle ray gliding through calm blue water on graceful wings, looking like some huge undersea bird. Usually, though, you'll see smaller rays lying half-buried in sandy areas near the reef. Some rays have poisonous spines at the bases of their tails, but they won't sting unless seriously molested—so don't step on one. At right, a southern stingray.

Enter the Supermale

For unclear reasons, certain parrotfish species feature three sexes: females, males, and terminal-phase males, or supermales. Supermales tend to be substantially larger than their nonsuper brethren and to boast more vivid colors. Some scientists think that supermales are females that have changed their sex.

Remoras

It's impossible to think about these bullet-shaped fish without thinking of the sharks in whose company they're almost always seen. Using a remarkable suction disk on the flat top of its head, a remora attaches itself to a shark's belly or side, saving energy by not moving independently, and feasting on scraps of food that evade the shark's great maw.

Fish that often accompany sharks and other large fish, eating their crumbs, are called commensals, a term meaning "those that eat at the same table." (For more on commensal feeding, see Chapter Three, page 69.) Above, a juvenile remora.

Scorpionfish

Call it a scorpionfish, a dragonfish, or a lionfish, and you know you're dealing with a formidable foe. These bottom-dwelling creatures, all of the same family, are characterized by a lumpy appearance, long fringed spines, and possession of some of the most potent venom of any animal on earth.

The fringed fins of some scorpionfish, such as those of the weedy scorpionfish of the Indo-Pacific, make the fish resemble seaweed. This perfect camouflage may be partly for self-defense, but it also helps the fish sneak up on and engulf unsuspecting prey. At left, a spotted scorpionfish.

Sea Stars

Better known as starfish, these echinoderms (which are closely related to the crinoids) are common inhabitants of every coral reef. One of the most spectacular sea stars of all, the blue sea star, is abundant on the Great Barrier Reef and other Indo-Pacific reefs. This velvety, vividly colored sea star is often seen lounging about on the reef, looking like a five-armed throw-cushion.

Sea stars, which are meat-eaters, have an other-worldly manner of feeding. A sea star will wrap its powerful arms around a mussel, for example, and pry the shell a little apart. Then, instead of trying to draw the mussel out of its shell, the sea star will actually extrude its own stomach through its mouth and insert it into the mussel's shell. Over the course of the next few hours, it will digest the hapless mussel, then pull its stomach back inside, and move on. At left, a multi-legged sun star.

Sea Turtles

Spotting a sea turtle on the reef is one of diving's great pleasures—and one that occurs far too infrequently. Their smooth, effortless movements, odd oarlike limbs, and benevolent expressions make sea turtles irresistible, as they cruise through the reef, constantly looking out for prey.

Oddly, you'll never see a baby sea turtle on a coral reef. In fact, you're unlikely to see one anywhere. Despite years of searching, scientists are still not sure where sea turtles spend the years that pass between hatching and maturity. Below, a green turtle.

Nesting Sea Turtles

For an unmatched natural-history experience, follow up your reef-side views of sea turtles with a visit to their beach nesting grounds. At such locations as Tortuguero, on the Caribbean coast of Costa Rica, you can see the great turtles haul themselves onto the beach, slowly dig a nest, then lay their clutch of eggs.

Sea Urchins

Always searching for more spectacular reef life, divers frequently look past such humbler reef denizens as the sea urchins. Take the time for a closer look, though, and you'll see that these echinoderms, which are relatives of sea stars, can be spectacular in their own right. Green, red, purple, with spines that can reach one foot (30 cm) in length, these slow-moving predators are often nocturnal and can startle night divers with their abundance. At right, a pencil urchin.

Sharks

Most sharks aren't reef-dwellers, but, like many predators, they do visit the reefs to take advantage of the abundant supply of food. Most experienced snorkelers or divers eventually acquire their very own shark story.

Not all sharks are dangerous. For example, if you see a slim-bodied shark with a long, scythelike tail lying motionless on the sandy bottom near the reef, chances are you've glimpsed a nurse shark. Although they can reach fourteen feet (4.2 m) in length, these common sharks are unaggressive, and they do not attack humans.

It should be obvious, though, that all sharks should be treated with extreme caution. No matter how beautiful the reef, if a smart diver finds it inhabited by large, unfamiliar sharks, he or she knows to leave. Above, white-tipped reef sharks.

Snappers

Most of us are familiar with snappers at the sushi bar or on the dinner table: They're undoubtedly among the most delicious fish in the sea. But for those visiting the ocean, snappers are medium-size—most reaching no more than ten pounds (4.5 kg)—toothy fish frequently seen speeding past more sedentary inhabitants of the reef. Below, a schoolmaster snapper.

Early Risers

You don't have to be a night diver to spot a squirrelfish or one of the reef's other nocturnal inhabitants. But you do have to be willing to get up early or to postpone dinner. Many of the reef's nocturnal fish begin emerging from their daytime resting places just before dusk, and don't return until after first light. Get to the reef early or late enough, and you'll get an unmatched opportunity to watch "the changing of the guard."

Squirrelfish

Once you begin to become familiar with the web of reef life, you'll learn to predict a fish's behavior and habits merely by taking a glance at it. For example, the tooth-filled jaws of barracudas and needlefish reveal that they are clearly predators, and the coloration of flounders and rays shows that they rely on camouflage for their protection. Similarly, squirrelfish's physical characteristics are well adapted to their habits, revealing that they are fish that only come out at night. Along with pink bodies and spiny dorsal fins, squirrelfish have some of the largest, darkest eyes relative to their size of any fish on the reef. Eyes like these clearly enable these fish to seek their prey in the dimmest conditions. Above, blackbar soldierfish.

Surgeonfish

Surgeonfish get their name from the scalpel-like spines they keep hidden in sheaths on either side of their tails. One slash with a needle-sharp spine, and even the most ferocious predator will learn to stay away.

The best-known surgeonfish are the tangs, disk-shaped, bright yellow or blue fish frequently seen in small schools on or above the reef. At left, a blue tang.

Triggerfish

Everything about triggerfish is distinctive. Shaped like diamonds adorned with streaming fins, they swim with butterfly-like strokes of their fins. Their markings are also unique; the clown triggerfish, pictured below, with its orange mouth, black-and-orange back, and array of brilliant white stripes and spots, may be the most garish fish on any reef. Divers can spot them in deeper, darker sections of Pacific reefs.

Triggerfish get their name from a tall spine located on their backs above the eyes. The spine lies inconspicuously along a triggerfish's back, until a predator or some other threat approaches. Then the triggerfish will head for the nearest crevice, wedge itself in, raise the spine, and lock it erect with a remarkable bony "trigger" located in the fish's spine. Not even the fiercest predator will be able to pry the firmly wedged fish out.

One of triggerfish's most distinctive characteristics is the placement of the eyes, set inches back from the beaked mouth. Triggerfish eat sea urchins, which are equipped with sharp, often poisonous spines, so it makes sense that triggerfish's eyes are located safely away from their mouths.

Trumpetfish

One of the most charming inhabitants of any Caribbean reef, the trumpetfish is a master of camouflage. Its languid movements and long, slender shape make it easily mistaken for fronds of sea grass. The trumpetfish can often be seen floating head-down amid sea whips and other plantlike corals, waiting for unwary shrimp and small fish to swim by.

The trumpetfish's shape and movements aren't its only forms of deception. It can also change color on demand. Trumpetfish can be seen trailing behind a slow-moving school of yellow tangs, wearing a bright yellow head to match the color of the tangs, while the rest of its body remains a mottled brownish color. Below, a yellow trumpetfish.

Wrasses

The wrasses are one of the most diverse of all fish families. Cruising above a Caribbean reef, it's hard to imagine that the gaudy, six-inch (15-cm) bluehead—with its vivid blue head and green body—and the hulking, dull-gray, three-foot-(1-m-) long hogfish belong to the same family. But they do.

Take a quick trip to an Indo-Pacific reef, and you may be in for an even greater shock. Here resides the giant Maori wrasse, a seven-foot-(2-m-) long hump-headed fish that bears an unsettling resemblance to Frankenstein's monster. At right, a Maori wrasse.

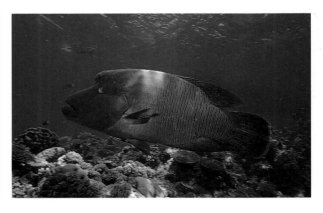

CHAPTER THREE:

The
Secret
Life
of the
Reef

Knowing some of the animals you're likely to encounter on the coral reef is an essential first step to a fuller, richer understanding of the marvelous reef ecosystem. But it's only a first step.

Compared to the full expanse of the oceans, which cover more than two-thirds of the earth's surface and average an astounding twelve thousand feet (3,600 m) in depth, the area covered by coral reefs is minuscule. Yet, the reefs are one of the most crowded environments on earth, with thousands of individual creatures of hundreds of different species often battling to survive in an area little larger than a square city block.

In the first section of Chapter Three, you'll journey through a typical day on a Caribbean coral reef, and you'll witness how its many species survive by working different shifts in this busy environment.

Then, in the next section, you'll learn about other remarkable adaptations that these creatures have developed to survive and coexist in the crowded, competitive reef environment: their use of symbiosis and commensalism, their predatory habits, their use of camouflage techniques, and other extraordinarily creative—and often little-known—behaviors.

A DAY IN THE LIFE OF A CORAL REEF

Bonaire is an arid island, but its reef gardens are among the lushest in the Caribbean.

Imagine that it's your first visit to the exciting underwater world of a coral reef. And pretend—though it is, in reality, physically and technologically impossible—that you'll be able to spend a full twenty-four hours on the reef.

You've just arrived at Bonaire, a small island located north of the Venezuelan coast. Despite this Caribbean island's unusual appearance—Bonaire boasts barren, rocky slopes adorned with cacti—you're excited to be here.

Bonaire is famous because it is entirely surrounded by beautiful, undisturbed fringing reefs. The entire island is a protected marine park and spearfishing has been outlawed for more than twenty years. So, Bonaire's reefs still harbor their full complement of fish, many of which have grown unafraid of humans. It's the perfect place for your first reef adventure.

You make your initial acquaintance with the reef in the late morning. You splash into the warm, clear ocean and soon are floating in about twenty feet (6 m) of water, eager to begin exploring the reef. First, you have to wait for your eyes to adjust to the colors, shapes, and movements all around you. Then, you begin to distinguish the coral you've spent some time learning about on land. Surrounding you like a vast, bony forest are stands of staghorn and elkhorn corals, while below you a gigantic brain coral rests on the bottom.

Most of the corals look dead, like ancient skeletal limestone; but the corals are, in fact, very much alive. Coral polyps don't feed during the day, so right now the polyps' tentacles remain withdrawn, hidden from view. Daytime is spent soaking up the sunlight, allowing the tiny zooxanthellae living within the polyps to do their essential work of photosynthesis.

Off in the distance, the water grows deeper, darker, and more mysterious, and the stands of staghorn coral are replaced by gloriously delicate green sea fans and other soft corals, all gently waving in the current. Beyond them, perhaps a hundred feet (30 m) away, the bottom suddenly plunges away into darkness at what seems like a 45-degree angle. This is the blue edge, where the ocean falls from about sixty feet (18 m) to hundreds of feet in depth. Immediately, you feel yourself drawn to this abyss, but you resist the impulse, for there's too much to see right here.

You tear your gaze away from the blue edge and begin to notice the fish inhabiting the reef nearby. If you're a typical newcomer to the reef, you are probably overwhelmed at first, for in one instant you see more fish, and more different types of fish, than you ever imagined. You're sure you'll never be able to tell what they all are.

A good way to make sense of all that you see on the reef is to divide its inhabitants into categories. Fish differ greatly in size, shape, and behavior; you just have to know what to look for.

First, you look for the abundant fish that seem to be just grazing and browsing peacefully around the reef. You distinguish schools of blue tangs, which graze casually along patches of reef, simultaneously relaxed and wary of unseen predators. Nearby, a pair of yellowtail damselfish dart out from a coral cranny and chase away a laggardly tang, while a beautiful French angelfish picks at a sponge.

Parrotfish are among the most distinctive fish on Bonaire's daytime reefs.

Next, you distinguish voracious eaters that stand out from all of the rest: large blue, midnight, and rainbow parrotfish. As you hang quietly in ten feet (3 m) of water, you can see the parrotfish rasping at the reef, making clearly audible crunching sounds as they convert dead patches of reef into sand.

Eventually, you will be able to distinguish another category of grazers: the variety of midwater feeders seeking the minute zooplankton that so many reef inhabitants, including the corals themselves, depend on for survival. Drifting past a staghorn grove, you get good looks at many of Bonaire's

characteristic daytime midwater feeders. Sergeant majors, those smartly striped damselfish, cruise in their constant search for zooplankton. Over the murky depths of the blue edge, clouds of blue and brown chromises (two more types of damselfish) and creole wrasses dip and twirl in the current.

In any environment, no matter how peaceful the scene, the grazers and browsers always have predators; watchful and wary, they are always aware that danger lurks nearby. On the reef, you are sure to see this struggle between hunter and hunted. For example, you may see a school of chromises which, sensing danger, will suddenly turn and flash away. You might not spot anything that could have startled them—or you might glimpse a barracuda cruising by.

Meanwhile, other predators seek smaller prey. Butterflyfish cruise the coral in search of marine worms and small crustaceans. That school of blue-striped grunts is on the lookout for shrimp and other crustaceans. And that small, beautiful spotted moray, no more than three feet (1 m) in length, would welcome a butterflyfish or grunt as a meal, if only one would swim by its coral hiding place.

As dusk approaches, you feel your pulse begin to quicken. The depths beyond the blue edge turn deep gray, then black. The last sharply angled

ray of sunlight flares against the reaching fingers of staghorn coral. Deeper, the brain corals glow whitely, as if gently illuminated from within. The sea fans and soft corals, so gaudy in daylight, become ghostly gray.

This is the time that many of the reef's most voracious predators, including jacks, groupers, and barracudas, begin to hunt more actively. Paradoxically, the dwindling light silhouettes the daytime grazers and browsers, making them easier to spot and to kill. In addition, the daytime fish are likely to be weary, while the nighttime species will still be groggy from sleep. Both will be less wary than usual and more vulnerable to hunting.

As if realizing their vulnerability to the predators, the tangs, parrotfish, and other smaller fish begin to cluster together and to make short, nervous, almost random forays across the face of the reef. Gradually they move downward toward the shadowy coral stands, unobtrusively seeking the protection of the deeper shadows.

While you were watching this activity, the chromises that had spent the day above the blue edge disappeared—where could so many fish go so quickly? Then you see what drove the chromises away: a breathtaking school of predatory jacks, streamlined and graceful. They flash silver in the waning light and then speed away, searching for other feeding grounds.

Morays are ferocious in appearance but harmless unless threatened. The spotted moray (above) is a daytime inhabitant of the reef. But its relative, the green moray, is a predator on the nighttime reef.

Down below on the reef, other familiar daytime fish have begun to find their nighttime resting places. Blue tangs, which look gray in the dusk, wedge themselves into tiny crevices, while the parrotfish find larger nooks. Here the parrotfish will surround themselves with a shroud made of mucous, which is distasteful to predators, in order to spend a safe night.

But the reef is not deserted following the bedding down of the chromises, tangs, and parrotfish. Instead, a new group of creatures that were unseen throughout the height of the day begin to appear. Masses of zooplankton, which have spent the day in deeper waters or hiding in coral crannies, rise toward the surface. Following them are small predators, which in turn attract larger meat-eaters, all helping to make up the nighttime food chain.

Above the reef is a school of six-inch- (15-cm-) long squid, speeding through the water like tiny torpedos, seeking food. Their extended tentacles and jellylike bodies show that these fragile, almost crystalline animals are not fish. They're actually mollusks, like clams and mussels, and they are most closely related to the octopus and cuttlefish.

Blue tangs are among the most beautiful of Bonaire's inhabitants, their midnight coloration blending in with the muted colors of deeper sections of the reef.

Hanging in the black water, you turn your torchlight on the squid, and for a moment you think you're hallucinating. Waves of iridescence—now blue, now red, now a whole rainbow of colors—run across the excited squids' bodies. Then, panicking at the unexpected glare, one ejects a cloud of bluish ink into the beam of your lantern, and while you're admiring the way the cloud spreads and disperses in the tidal surge, the squid dart from view.

But there's plenty else to see on the nighttime reef. Down below, amid the coral, you begin to spot increasing numbers of gaudy red and hot-pink fish with huge, black eyes and cryptic white markings. These are the squirrelfish, a group of medium-size (about five to fifteen inches [13 to 38 cm] in length), nocturnal predators that are among the most dominant fish on Bonaire's reef at night.

The squirrelfish's large, light-sensitive eyes make them well equipped to navigate the reef at night. But even their seemingly garish coloration serves a purpose. Except in the brightest of lights, water filters out the red wavelengths of the color spectrum. Thus, in the dark water, the squirrelfish seem gray or black, easily evading the notice of potential prey. By breaking up the visible outlines of the fish's form, the white markings sported by many species make the camouflage even more effective.

As you watch a longspine squirrelfish patrol the reef, your gaze is suddenly drawn by a far larger, more ominous form, barely glimpsed from the corner of your eye. For a moment you can't find it, but then you spot it snaking along between two coral heads, and you have to force yourself not to swim toward the surface.

Dawn and dusk see the intermingling of nocturnal species like the pink longspine squirrelfish, and daytime denizens like the blue-striped grunt.

While daytime visitors to the reef will see only the closed skeleton of this *Tubastrea* tree coral, night divers will have the privilege of witnessing the gloriously beautiful polyps of this coral species.

It's a moray. You may have gotten a look at a spotted moray earlier. But that three-foot (1-m) creature, besides belonging to the same family, is nothing like the massive animal you are seeing now. This is a green moray, the largest, most powerful of all Caribbean morays. The one that has now turned its gimlet eyes and gaping, tooth-ridden jaws in your direction is at least six feet (2 m) long. Even more awe-inspiring is the eel's extraordinarily thick, muscular body. Compact and powerful, it is nearly unrivalled in its mastery of the nighttime world that is its domain.

When the moray has swum out of the range of your flashlight, you begin to notice that something about the landscape of the reef has changed. It takes a moment to figure out what it is, but then you realize that the coral appears to be blooming. During the day, the coral heads seem virtually lifeless. Brain corals look like huge, whorled boulders; staghorns like trees in winter; sheet corals like bare plates; and star corals like hunks of lava left behind by some ancient volcano. Daytime is for absorbing sunlight so that the zooxanthellae can do their work.

But the reef is transformed at night. With the rise of the zooplankton from the depths, it's time for the coral polyps to extend their tentacles in order to trap these tiny animals. The corals that only hours before seemed like hunks of dead rock now take on a fuzzy, almost diaphanous appearance, half-hidden behind a shimmering screen of waving tentacles. But the true glory of the reef at night is the coral polyps' rarely seen colors: deepest pink, gentle orange, vivid yellow—nearly every color of the rainbow can be seen in this hidden, secret garden.

Bewitched by the beauty of the nighttime reef and its inhabitants, you lose track of time. Suddenly you notice that the water all around you has subtly shifted in tone, from an impenetrable black to a shade of gray. That actively feeding staghorn below has once again turned to stone. The sun has just risen above the eastern horizon.

As you watch, the reef environment grows steadily, rapidly brighter. The last squirrelfish hurry for the best hiding places. The green moray is nowhere to be seen. You can't see them, but you know that the zooplankton too have left the reef environs, heading over the blue edge to deeper waters. A pair of midnight parrotfish materialize next to a stand of elkhorn. The first brown chromises assume their sentry duty above the rim of the blue edge. A nassau grouper casts a hungry eye at a school of tangs. A barracuda comes over to take a look at you.

The daytime shift has begun once again.

SURVIVING ON THE REEF

During your day on Bonaire's coral reef, you caught a glimpse of the engine that drives the reef inhabitants: hunger. Almost every behavior and almost every adaptation is designed either to help reef animals obtain food, or to enable them to escape detection and thus avoid becoming food.

The crowded world of the coral reef presents challenges both to the hunter and to the hunted. The reef is filled with hiding places: Every coral head has nooks, crannies, crevices, and caves that provide instant and effective hiding places for fish. Watch a damselfish dart between the plates of a sheet coral, somehow inserting itself into a slot that seems no more than a

few millimeters across, and you'll realize how frustrating hunting on the reef must be to barracudas, groupers, and other large predators.

Yet, the first thing you noticed on your daylong reef jaunt was how popular the reef was with those predators. No active reef escapes the notice of the ocean's premier hunters: sharks, jacks, and others, in addition to groupers and barracudas. Survival is a chancy proposition for prey species on a coral reef; if they stray a few inches too far from the nearest hiding place, they'll become a meal.

As a result of this eternal push-and-pull between hunter and hunted, reef fish have devised spectacular means of both offense and defense. Watching the reef survival game can be as fascinating as following a game of chess; but, like chess, this battle can only be marveled at by those who truly understand what they're seeing.

Most sharks, including the bull shark above, don't inhabit reefs, but they often visit them in search of a quick, easy meal. Although nearly always found near coral, darting among its nooks and crannies, damselfish like the one below actually eat algae, sponges, and tiny animals—not the coral itself.

This diver has been lucky enough to spot a peacock flounder—a master of camouflage against the sandy sea floor.

Camouflage and mimicry, the arts of evading detection by fading into the background or by closely resembling something else, are probably the most basic means of survival in nearly every environment on earth.

Walk through a field in the northeastern United States in early summer, and you might almost stumble over the fawn of a white-tailed deer, its white stripes and spots making it almost impossible to see in its grassy hiding place. The fawn's camouflage is nearly perfect, but not as perfect as the camouflage employed by the birds, insects, and other creatures that you didn't even notice during your walk.

Several different types of camouflage have been taken to extraordinary lengths—by both hunters and hunted—on the coral reef. Perhaps the most common strategy is the use of cryptic camouflage, in which a reef animal so closely resembles a part of the scenery that it becomes virtually invisible. The animal can then avoid being detected by its predators or sneak up unnoticed on its prey.

Prey species that use cryptic camouflage include the peacock flounder, which can change its color to match the sandy or rocky sea floor where it hides, and the remarkable juvenile leatherjacket (an Indo-Pacific filefish), which mimics a piece of silt-covered seaweed. And the cryptic camouflage used by predators may be even more brilliant. The longlure frogfish of the Caribbean is a remarkably lumpy, warty fish with a bright orange color. The result is that it looks exactly like any of a number of sponges found in its reef-floor habitat near the blue edge.

In addition to camouflage, the frogfish adds yet another subterfuge to its arsenal. The first spine of the fish's dorsal fin resembles a small fishing rod, tipped with a fleshy white lure. The frogfish wiggles the lure until an unwary small fish swims by. Then, with a mighty gulp, the frogfish snaps up its unsuspecting prey.

Many other reef predators have also evolved clever camouflage techniques. The fins of lionfish and scorpionfish, for example, are festooned in spiky protuberances that resemble fronds of seaweed. Resting on the bottom, they simply wait for a small fish to swim within range, and then engulf it with a mighty gulp of their powerful jaws.

The trumpetfish of the Caribbean reefs has perfected a double method of sneaking up on its prey. Floating head-down, it looks like nothing more than a sea whip; or, by changing color to match common reef fish, it can become lost among the school of tangs or other plant-eaters. In both cases, the trumpetfish's prey doesn't spot its nemesis until it's too late.

Not every form of camouflage requires close resemblance to a fish, sponge, or other facet of the reef environment. Butterfly fish, juvenile angelfish, and many other species are garbed in seemingly garish stripes and spots, often in inconsistent patterns of black and white or various colors. To a hunting predator, this coloration serves to disrupt the natural body outline of the prey fish. The predator, unsure of what it's seeing, may hesitate for a moment, giving the prey time to escape.

A diver who spends enough time on the reef soon notices that many reef fish, as well as almost every open-ocean species, contain the same basic color pattern: Their belly and other underparts are white or gray, while their upperparts are darker. There's a convincing explanation for this com-

mon pattern. If a fish swims above your head while you're diving, you'll notice that its light underparts blend in with the silvery surface. The reverse also holds true: Look down at a fish, and you'll see that the fish's upperparts are hidden against the darker colors of the deeper water or sea floor.

While many reef creatures use such cryptic coloration to remain unseen, others announce their presence with bright—almost garish—colors. There can be different reasons for this type of camouflage. When threatened, some gaily hued fish, such as cowfish and boxfish, have the ability to secrete powerful poisons through their skin. And some brightly colored immature angelfish carry concealed spines. These creatures' brilliant colors serve as a warning that they would not make a pleasant meal.

Certain nonpoisonous fish mimic the bright coloration of the showy, toxic species as a method of gaining protection for themselves. For example, baby surgeonfish, which are comparatively defenseless, often mimic young angelfish, which have tougher skin and a less savory taste, in order to trick predators into leaving them alone.

Other forms of mimicry on the reef also depend on the fish, or certain of its features, standing out and being seen. Many brightly colored juvenile fish, as well as adult butterfly fish, sport large spots on their flanks. These are "false eyes," which serve the double purpose of frightening away smaller predators and befuddling larger ones into attacking the fish's rear instead of its head, giving it a better chance to escape.

Of course, even the best camouflage and mimicry can only help reef fish survive. Even the smallest species, in addition to staying alive, must also find their own food—a task which can be a challenge in the reef's intensely competitive environment. Many reef species have risen to the challenge by developing some of the most fascinating methods of survival found anywhere in the natural world.

Top: The four-eye butterflyfish and many other butterflyfish rely on their "false eyes" to scare away or confuse potential predators. Above: Its warty orange body and slumped posture mimicking a large sponge, the long-lure frogfish dangles a tiny lure, attracting the smaller fish that serve as its food.

Although one bite from these morays' powerful jaws would spell doom for the brightly colored cleaner shrimp, the shrimp are never harmed as they pick fungus and parasites from the eels' skin.

SYMBIOSIS

In general, different animal species don't cooperate; they are either competing with one another, or ignoring one another. This rule is as true on the reef as anywhere else. Grunts and butterflyfish may tolerate each other, goatfish and tangs may even swim in the same school, but in general the populous reef environment is made up of countless species with a solitary goal: survival.

However, in certain well-known cases, individuals of different reef species actually work together toward the common goal of survival, with each species benefiting in some way from the relationship. This process is called symbiosis, and it is also found among certain dry-land species.

The entire world of a coral reef actually depends on symbiosis. Remember that the polyps of nearly every reef-building coral, including such dominant species as staghorn, elkhorn, and brain corals, host tiny algae called zooxanthellae. The polyps provide a place to live and access to sunlight, while the zooxanthellae, through photosynthesis, return oxygen and food to the coral. This is a clear example of symbiosis.

Of the other examples of symbiosis on the reef, perhaps the most intriguing involves not two, but many different species. This is the process known as cleaning symbiosis, and it occurs every day on every reef on earth. In cleaning symbiosis, large fish, including many meat-eaters, allow small fish to "clean" them—that is, to pick tiny parasites and fungus from their skin. Such "cleaner" fish are allowed all over the larger fish's bodies, including into their mouths, without any danger of being eaten.

The reason for this suspension of the normal predator-prey relationship is simple. Both species clearly benefit from the symbiotic relationship: The cleaner fish gain an easy meal, while the big fish gain relief from annoying parasites and fungus, which might otherwise eventually harm their health.

Dozens of species of fish, as well as certain shrimp, act as cleaner species. These include both the juveniles of angelfish, butterflyfish, and other well-known species, and the adults of some small species, such as wrasses and gobies. The cleaner wrasse, a common species on many Atlantic reefs, has been named for this talent, while a full six species of gobies found on Indo-Pacific reefs go by the group name of cleaning gobies.

Perhaps the most interesting element of cleaning symbiosis is that many cleaning species don't need to search for clients. Instead, individuals of several different species set up "cleaning stations," staking out a specific rock or piece of coral and waiting for the parasite-ridden bigger fish to come to them. It's not unusual for a snorkeler to come upon a group of boxfish, parrotfish, and other larger species waiting in a peaceful line for their turn at the cleaning station. Meanwhile, the cleaner species work industriously on those at the front of the line.

The presence of these cleaning stations is very important. When scientists on Bonaire captured and removed the cleaning species from a reef, the overall number of fish on the reef plummeted. Weeks later, the number was still lower than normal, and many of the fish that remained were ridden with parasites and fungus.

Cleaning symbiosis is not the only form of symbiosis found on coral reefs. Perhaps the most spectacular—and best known—of all symbiotic relationships is the one between anemones and a group of damselfish called the clownfish, common throughout the Indo-Pacific. Like coral polyps, to which they are closely related, anemones boast tentacles armed with stinging nematocysts. With these venomous tentacles, the anemones capture prey

Cleaning gobies are among the most commonly seen inhabitants of cleaning stations on Caribbean reefs.

On some Indo-Pacific reefs, nearly every anemone has a resident clownfish, which remains unharmed by the deadly poison in its host's tentacles.

ranging from zooplankton to small fish. Even large fish avoid the tentacles, which might not be able to capture and kill them, but could cause them great distress.

Yet, instead of avoiding the anemones' stinging tentacles, the clownfish actively seek them out. In fact, even experienced divers rarely see a clownfish that isn't nestling amid the tentacles of an anemone—or at least swimming warily nearby. On some reefs, nearly every large anemone seems to harbor its own clownfish. Scientists once believed that clownfish were somehow immune to the anemones' venom, much as beekeepers sometimes become immune to bee stings. More recently, though, they've learned that the clownfish have actually evolved a far more clever approach. They aren't poisoned or killed by the venom because the anemones don't sting them.

Scientists have learned that the nematocysts in the anemones' tentacles are activated by a combination of physical contact and certain chemical triggers contained in mucous on the skin of fish and other prey animals. Divers can see that the clownfish clearly come into contact with the tentacles. So how do they avoid triggering the stinging cells?

First, the clownfish stay unharmed by producing a mucous that doesn't trigger the anemones' nematocysts. Second, the fish carry this subterfuge even further by coating their bodies with the mucous produced by the anemone itself. The anemone, which is conditioned not to sting itself, simply doesn't recognize the clownfish as potential food.

Clearly, the clownfish benefits from this relationship, by obtaining one of the safest havens anywhere on the reef. In return, the anemone mày get scraps of the clownfish's food, but scientists aren't sure if this is, in fact, the benefit that the anemones gain from the relationship.

COMMENSALISM

Not every interspecies relationship is mutually beneficial. Some feature small fish that accompany large predators, such as sharks, swordfish, and groupers, and sneak fragments of food left behind by these messy meat-eaters.

These fish are collectively known as commensals, which means "those who dine at the same table." Perhaps the most famous and most cleverly adapted of all commensals are the remoras, torpedo-shaped fish equipped with a sucker atop their heads. These fish, commonly known as "shark-suckers," attach themselves with their suckers to a shark's belly, and they'll be carried to where the food is without having to expend any energy of their own.

Another group of well-known commensals are the pilotfish, free-swimming black-and-white banded members of the jack family. Despite their common name, pilotfish are not likely to pilot their host predators to food, but only to follow them to where the food is.

One of the best-known examples of commensalism is seen in pilotfish, who follow sharks (like this white-tip), eating the crumbs left behind after a shark feast.

A diver who hangs motionless above a coral reef might think at first that the reef contains a confusing, chaotic mass of life. Clouds of sergeant majors and chromises flood the clear water above the reef, parrotfish and grunts seem to be grazing at every coral head, and smaller species are darting and weaving everywhere.

But a diver who takes a little time on the reef will soon realize that many reef species actually stake out and fiercely defend territories, ranging from a few square feet to an entire coral head. What makes this behavior hard to distinguish is that the territorial fish will often only defend its territory from other members of its own species, and not from the crowds of other species passing through.

The territoriality of reef fish should not be surprising; every ecosystem on earth is composed of countless large-to-tiny territories. A pack of wolves may patrol a stretch of tundra covering hundreds of square miles, while a sparrow singing in your backyard during nesting season is announcing its "ownership" of the thicket containing its nest.

Damselfish are among the most territorial of all reef fish, fearlessly chasing away all intruders of their home range.

Territoriality even occurs where it would seem impossible: in the open ocean, thousands of feet below the surface and thousands of feet above the sea floor. In this seemingly barrierless environment, certain fish may establish a territory around floating seaweed, around giant relatives of the jellyfish called siphonophores (which can reach thirty feet [9 m] in length), or even around a plume of silt. The next day the entire territory may have drifted several miles, but the fish will still be defending it.

Most snorkelers and divers first notice territoriality on the coral reef when a damselfish comes darting out of a coral nook and pugnaciously tries to evict them. Only once the intruder has swum beyond some unseen border will the damselfish return to its lair. Many different species, including certain angelfish, butterflyfish, and others are also territorial, if not so brazen about it.

As in other ecosystems, the finest territories on the reef are the ones that contain the best food supply and the most secure hiding places. Therefore, larger, stronger, and more dominant members of a species will usually take the best territories and attract the strongest mates. Remarkably, some species, particularly damselfish, will even "farm" the algae within their territory. Each day, they'll patrol their farms, removing larger, unsavory types of algae and allowing smaller, tastier ones to grow unimpeded.

Despite the seemingly aggressive nature of damselfish and other reef denizens, territoriality actually discourages serious fights. Two damselfish meeting at the borders of their adjoining territories will rush back and forth, raise their fins, and open their mouths, brandishing tiny teeth—but they barely touch each other. The presence of territories helps to keep the peace on the coral reef.

Not all fish are individually territorial: Many (including these grunts) seem perfectly willing to live in the close quarters of a school.

BREEDING

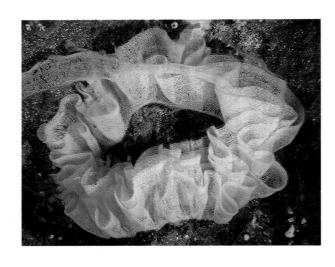

In general, coral-reef fish breed like all other fish. The female releases into the water an egg mass containing hundreds or thousands of eggs, and the male produces enough sperm to fertilize the mass. The male and female abandon the eggs so, upon hatching, the minuscule young are on their own. Hundreds die for each one that lives, but so many eggs are produced that enough survive for the species to thrive.

Certain reef fish, however, employ remarkable—even outlandish—variations on the basic breeding technique. Perhaps most bizarre are the fish, such as parrotfish, bass, and others that change sex during their lifespan, often beginning as females and then later transforming into males. Some species, such as the Atlantic harlequin bass, can even boast working sexual organs of both sexes simultaneously, although a single individual cannot impregnate itself.

Perhaps the most spectacular example of sex change in the fish world concerns the blue-and-gold angelfish, native to the Great Barrier Reef and other Indo-Pacific reefs. These gorgeous fish generally live in groups of four to seven, made up of one male and a small harem of females. The male patrols the borders of the group's territory, drives off competing males, and mates with all the females (usually during the summer, just before sunset). But, when the male dies, he is not replaced with a competitor or a group from a nearby territory. Instead, the largest female will change sex, take over the role of the dominant male, and maintain the remaining females as its harem.

Other breeding rituals are less unusual, but still differ from those practiced by most reef fish. For example, while the laying and fertilization of the eggs usually constitute the end of the parents' responsibilities, most damselfish are far more protective. Just as they establish, tend, and fiercely protect their algae gardens, damselfish males will actively guard the eggs, which are attached to rocks within their territories.

Other fish take these protective habits even further. The male yellowhead jawfish of Atlantic reefs, for example, carries the eggs in its mouth until they hatch. When it needs to eat, the jawfish will carefully place the eggs in a small burrow in the sand and retrieve them once it's finished.

Male sea horses, as well as their close relatives the pipefish, also carry the eggs until hatching—and even beyond. Unlike the jawfish, however, these ancient, bony fish that are found on reefs worldwide have evolved special pouches to brood the eggs. After mating, the female deposits the fertilized eggs in the male's pouch. The eggs remain in the pouch for several weeks; hours to days after hatching, the male will expel the tiny, perfectly formed young, which must then fend for themselves.

In contrast, the lack of parental care after egg-laying in some fish species actually contributes to the spread of the species to new reefs. For example, the eggs of the coney, an Atlantic grouper, and of many other species are pelagic, meaning that they are ocean-going. After being spawned, the eggs join the mass of zooplankton drifting on the currents. The eggs may drift for a month and travel hundreds of miles. Upon hatching, the baby fish will instinctively begin swimming toward the nearest reef. There they will continue to grow, eventually mating and beginning the process again.

Sea horses boast one of the most remarkable breeding techniques of any species of life on earth.

CHAPTER FOUR:

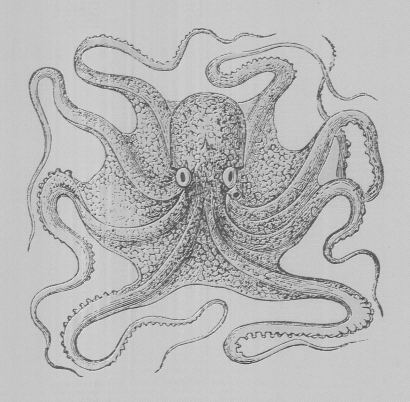

The World's Best Coral Reefs

It would be impossible to cover all the reefs in the world in one chapter, or even in one entire book. The Philippines alone, for example, includes thousands of islands, nearly every one of which boasts a fringing reef. This chapter covers the finest and most popular reef destinations in the earth's oceans and seas. It concentrates on one (or a couple) of the most beautiful, spectacular, and unusual reefs at each location. The areas covered should give even the most ambitious snorkeler or diver information about a multitude of the greatest reef sites, and enable him or her to form goals to fill a lifetime of spectacular exploration.

Located less than sixty miles (96 km) off this beautiful beach on Belize is the gorgeous Lighthouse Reef, home to an abundance of reef wildlife.

THE ATLANTIC OCEAN: THE WORLD'S MOST ISOLATED REEFS

In general, the Atlantic Ocean deserves its reputation as a cold, rough ocean, populated by sturdy open-sea fish and other creatures accustomed to its frigidity and turbulence. One area, however, can boast some of the most beautiful reefs on earth: the southwest Atlantic, home to the Caribbean Sea.

The Atlantic reefs are the most unusual of all the world's coral domains. Warmed by the Gulf Stream, separated by Central America from the vast expanses of the Pacific, and hemmed in by the cold, deep ocean on the east, the marine inhabitants of the Atlantic reefs have evolved in virtual isolation for more than a million years.

As a result, these reefs host many species not found on Indo-Pacific reefs, while certain Pacific species (notably, the crown-of-thorns starfish and sea snakes) have never been found in the Caribbean. Even the look of the reefs differs between the two oceans: Pacific reefs tend to be low-slung and densely packed, while the Caribbean is home to tall, delicately branching staghorn and elkhorn corals.

Anyone interested in coral reefs should know about the diving and snorkeling possibilities to be found in the Atlantic. An educated reef visitor will know how to skip the overhyped, overexpensive dives on badly used, deteriorating reefs, offered by many islands, and will concentrate instead on some of the Atlantic's remaining glories.

Aruba

While Bonaire gains most of the attention (see Chapter Three, page 56 and below), its neighbor islands, Aruba and Curaçao, also offer some appealing diving. Aruba in particular has attractions not found on Bonaire, especially some spectacular wreck diving.

If you're visiting Aruba with diving in mind, you should not miss the wreck of the *Antilla*, a four-hundred-foot (120-m) German freighter sunk in 1940 in about sixty feet (18 m) of water. After more than half a century, the metal hull has become home to a breathtaking array of hard and soft corals, gaudy sponges, and endless schools of grunts, parrotfish, and other typical Caribbean reef denizens.

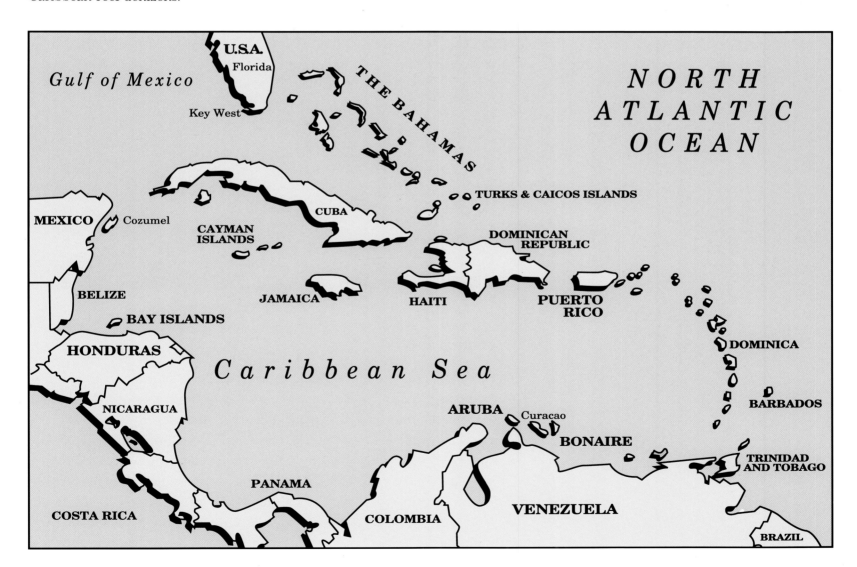

Bahamas

Fly over the Bahamas, and you'll notice immediately that these flat, sandy islands are surrounded by clear, calm water punctuated by miles of coral. Get away from Freeport, Paradise Island, and other overpopulated resorts, and you'll find some of the best diving in the Atlantic.

Don't miss the Tongue of the Ocean, a breathtaking chasm (formed by a split between two tectonic plates) that lies between New Providence and Andros islands. Few sensations are more thrilling—and sobering—than drifting over the reef, then suddenly emerging like a hang glider over a dark, bottomless abyss, and realizing that the ocean floor lies more than thirteen thousand feet (3,900 m) straight down.

Get away from the resorts, and you'll find that the Bahamas are home to some of the Atlantic's finest snorkeling and diving.

Barbados

Barbados is more than exclusive resorts and beautiful beaches. It also features unspoiled and seldom-visited reefs, vast schools of reef fish, and some of the most dramatic wrecks anywhere in the Atlantic.

Perhaps the most spectacular wreck of all is the *Stavronikita*, a 350-foot (105-m) freighter that was the victim of a fire, sunk intentionally off the west coast of Barbados in 1978. Today, the enormous hulk rests in 130 feet (39 m) of water (some parts of the ship rise to within 10 feet [3 m] of the surface), and it is covered by soft corals and home to schooling fish and other reef inhabitants.

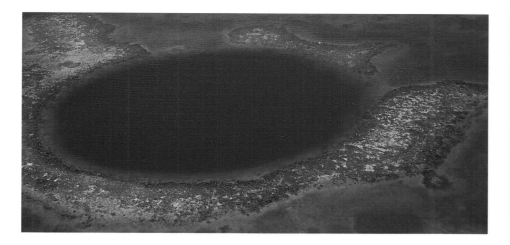

Belize

Belize has some of the most gloriously unspoiled reefs in the world. This tiny country, set just south of Mexico's far more famous Yucatán Peninsula, boasts the world's second longest barrier reef—most of which hasn't even been explored yet.

Belize's barrier reef is nearly 200 miles (320 km) in length, second in length and mass only to the Great Barrier Reef. As a further inducement, Belize's waters contain three of the four atoll systems found anywhere in the Caribbean: Lighthouse Reef, Glover's Reef, and the Turneffe Islands. Overall, this little-known country is host to as much as 350 linear miles (560 linear km) of reef, including many of the Caribbean's most beautiful caves, canyons, and immense coral stands.

Belize is also home to one of the few completely protected fringing reef environments on earth. The Hol Chan Marine Preserve, off the east-coast island resort Ambergris Caye, includes about five square miles (13 square km) of coral, sandy flats covered with sea grass, and mangrove swamps—all safe from coral robbers and fishermen.

At Hol Chan, divers can spot enormous, tame green morays, abundant groupers (grown quite huge and phlegmatic due to protection), and some of the largest parrotfish on earth. You'll have no trouble spotting any of these creatures, as long as you can see through the clouds of blue-striped grunts, snappers, and other schooling fish!

More enterprising divers, and those with a live-aboard dive boat for accommodations, have an even more spectacular destination awaiting them: the atoll at Lighthouse Reef, located sixty miles (96 km) offshore. These endless miles of shallow (often less than twenty feet [6 m] deep), exquisitely beautiful, and wildlife-rich reefs harbor such impressive—and often hard-to-find—fish as giant Nassau groupers, hogfish, and snappers.

Bonaire

If you have read Chapter Three, you already know that the entire island of Bonaire is a protected marine park, where no spearfishing or fish-trapping is permitted from the surface to a depth of two hundred feet (60 m). You already know that Bonaire's reefs are home to nearly every type of fish and other creature found on any Atlantic reef. You may even know that if you visit Bonaire with diving or snorkeling in mind, you'll find plenty of other people there who share your interests.

Belize's Other Attractions

No visitor to Belize should confine his or her visit to the reefs. This magnificent subtropical country, once a center of Mayan culture, also harbors gorgeous rain forests filled with parrots, monkeys, and numerous other creatures; ancient Mayan ruins; and a fascinating mix of cultures. A few extra days spent exploring these treasures, as well as the reefs, are well worth the time.

Belize's Blue Hole may be the most spectacular of the country's coral attractions, but don't miss the others—including the world's second longest barrier reef and some of the only atolls in the Atlantic.

You should also know that the leeside of Bonaire and its tiny companion island, Klein Bonaire, harbor nearly a hundred different marked dive sites, encompassing any undersea sight a diver could dream of. Just a few of the marvelous attractions are: Rappel, home to some of the densest concentrations of hard corals (including some remarkably large brain corals); Playa Funchi, just offshore from the arid expanses of Washington Slaagbai National Park; or any of a dozen pristine sites off Klein Bonaire.

Cayman Islands

Unlike Bonaire, the Cayman Islands, which comprise Grand Cayman, Little Cayman, and Cayman Brac, receive thousands of visitors each year who have no interest in snorkeling or diving. Located just south of Cuba, these are typical Caribbean resort islands, featuring boutique shopping, endless sandy beaches, and picture-postcard sunsets.

Snorkeler's Delight

Unlike the vast majority of the world's reefs, Bonaire's coral is easily accessible from shore. You don't need to plunge to a depth of sixty feet (18 m) or beyond to find undisturbed coral; you don't even need a boat. Just jump in nearly anywhere along the lee shore—off the Town Pier, the 1,000 Steps, or any of several resorts—and you'll immediately be surrounded by some of the loveliest reefs in the Caribbean.

Although Bonaire is a Caribbean island, its unusual terrain features barren, rocky slopes and cacti.

But don't be fooled. Divers have been raving about the Caymans' many and diverse reef treasures for years. You'd have to travel far to find much more exciting diving than occurs just off Grand Cayman, whose reefs form great walls, sometimes plunging from just below the surface to the sea floor hundreds of feet below. Perhaps the pinnacle of the Grand Cayman diving experience is North Wall, a twenty-mile (32-km) stretch of reef that begins at depths as shallow as twenty feet (6 m). One of North Wall's prime attractions is Tarpon Alley, a coral canyon inhabited by a huge, tame school of enormous tarpon.

While you're there, don't miss Eagle Ray Pass, consistently a good spot for seeing these huge, graceful rays. Other sites you should make the effort to visit are: Babylon, home to a 30-foot- (9-m-) thick coral pillar that sprouts from 180 feet (54 m) down to within 60 feet (18 m) of the surface, and Julie's Delight, which contains some of the thickest groves of rare black coral surviving anywhere on earth.

These schooling tarpon—open-ocean fish rarely seen on coral reefs—are one of the attractions of Grand Cayman's Tarpon Alley.

Cozumel

A small island located off the coast of Mexico's Yucatán Peninsula, and a short hop south from the famous resort of Cancun, Cozumel is one of the world's most visited diving and snorkeling destinations.

Unfortunately, the downside of Cozumel's accessibility is immediately apparent upon one's first glance at Palancar, the island's most famous reef. Visiting this great coral rampart, two miles (3 km) long and more than a thousand feet (300 m) deep, a diver would once have found luxuriant black coral gardens and huge groupers and other fish. But today the overwhelming first impression is of plunder and destruction. The black coral forest is gone, harvested to be transformed into cheap knicknacks and jewelry; the groupers have long since become dinner.

The Mexican government has finally begun to protect Palancar, which still plays host to a lively assortment of typical Caribbean reef fish. Even the black coral may return in all its glory—if only given enough time.

A typical deep-water Caribbean reef scene, dominated by gaudy *Tubastrea* corals.

Drifting Above Palancar

Perhaps the most unusual aspect of diving or snorkeling on Cozumel's reefs is the pervasive presence of a strong, steady current. This can make for easy, yet thrilling reef exploration, for few other sites allow you to cover so much distance on a single jaunt. But drifting can also be dangerous, both to you and to the reef.

Lose control and you may find yourself grabbing at the reef, uprooting coral, and destroying sponges and sea fans. Even greater are the dangers of losing buoyancy, drifting away from your buddy, and, in the worst case, running out of air. Any diver should make sure to prepare well and practice before visiting Palancar.

Dominica

Can you name a Caribbean island with no beaches? An island with dense, untracked rain forests filled with parrots and other exotic birds, the highest mountains of any Caribbean island, and spectacular underwater walls and pinnacles, challenging and thrilling even to the most expert divers? This is Dominica.

Dominica is home to perhaps the finest diving anywhere among the windward islands of the eastern Caribbean. Here are remarkably lush reefs, filled with schools of fish, brilliantly colored sponges, and other denizens of a healthy reef system. Best of all, these reefs remain virtually unvisited. On Dominica's reefs, you and your buddy may be the only divers for miles around!

Florida

As almost any diver or snorkeler knows, the Florida Keys are home to the continental United States' only coral reefs. Unfortunately, many of these reefs are also among the most heavily used, and abused, of any on earth. Coral stands broken by anchors, plundered by divers seeking mementos, or killed by runoff and pollution are all common sights.

Gorgonians and other soft corals are among the reef inhabitants now making a comeback on Cozumel's Palancar Reef, once one of the most beautiful reefs on earth.

The Mangrove World

While Key Largo National Marine Sanctuary protects the coral reefs from three to about seven miles (5 to 11 km) offshore, the zone from the shoreline to the sanctuary entrance is also protected under the auspices of John Pennekamp Coral Reef State Park. Pennekamp protects several environments crucial to the health of the reef, but none more so than the mangrove zone.

Anyone who snorkels the murky world of the mangroves will soon see why. This underwater forest provides sanctuary to what seems like every juvenile fish on the reef. Here are two-inch (5-cm) barracudas, just as testy and pugnacious as the giant adults. Here are also tiny angelfish, tangs, and damselfish. And some of the reef's most fascinating invertebrates, such as shrimp, worms, and nudibranchs, are home in the mangroves as well.

Yet it is still possible to find beautiful reefs in such protected areas as Key Largo and Loee Key National Marine Sanctuaries. At these locations, spearfishing is prohibited, and many mooring sites have been set up to protect the reefs from wayward anchors, resulting in diving and snorkeling that approach the glory they must have had in ages past.

Located near Big Pine Key, Loee Key N.M.S., established in 1981, encompasses little more than five square miles (13 square km). Yet even in this small area, the sanctuary contains a complete reef ecosystem: mangrove swamp, sandy sea-grass flats, and the reef itself.

Key Largo N.M.S., located just sixty miles (96 km) from Miami, is under substantially more pressure, in no small part due to the more than one

Coastal mangroves are an essential part of the reef ecosystem, providing food and shelter to young reef fish.

million snorkelers and divers who visit each year. Yet, despite the damage that such heavy use has inflicted, for those North Americans seeking an introduction to the joys of coral reef exploration, Key Largo can still provide abundant wildlife and beautiful reefs.

Honduras

Looking for perhaps the least-known, most exotic dive destination left in the Caribbean? Take a trip to the Bay Islands, a trio of unspoiled tropical islands located just a few miles off the coast of Honduras, but far enough away that they haven't been damaged by overdevelopment or fresh-water runoff.

Roatan, the largest of the three Bay Islands, is just three miles (5 km) wide by thirty miles (48 km) long. The island is flanked by narrow strips of reef, vulnerable to even the slightest pressure, bordered by dizzyingly abrupt drop-offs. In some areas, these abysses plunge nearly a thousand feet (300 m), almost straight down, leaving even the most daredevil diver with a sense of the sea's great power and mystery.

Puerto Rico

Puerto Rico is another heavily visited tourist destination whose offshore waters have suffered as a result. But the persistent diver can find some beautiful reefs here, including some that are unusual by Caribbean standards.

Don't miss The Reserve, located offshore from the growing resort town of Humacao. This reef features huge sandy channels snaking their way through the rich coral pinnacles at a depth of about eighty feet (24 m). Impressive schools of jacks and other large fish are common here.

Turks and Caicos

The Turks and Caicos are undoubtedly among the least-known islands in the entire Caribbean region. And that's exactly the way most avid divers want them to remain, because their very obscurity has made these thirty small islands one of the last, best dive destinations in the Atlantic.

Located south and east of the Bahamas, the English-speaking Turks and Caicos can boast more than two hundred miles (320 km) of white-sand beaches, underwater visibility that reaches two hundred feet (60 m), and spectacular coral walls plunging to more than a mile (1.6 km) in depth, pockmarked with dramatic gullies and canyons. On Providenciales (better known as Provo), the most developed island, such dive sites as Shark Hole, the Pinnacles, and Aquarium West provide a view of the glories of the Atlantic reef.

But if unspoiled coral, enormous manta rays and sea turtles, and endless schools of reef and open-ocean fish aren't enough, come to the Turks and Caicos in February and March. You're likely to spot humpback whales migrating through the deep Turks Island Passage that lies between the two island groups. At this time, these magnificent whales, which summer in the North Atlantic, are in the midst of their long migration south to their breeding grounds off the Dominican Republic.

Live-Aboard Dive Boats

Any diver knows the routine. Wake up in a beachside hotel or hostel, eat breakfast, gather the gear, collect on the dock, board the boat, and head for the dive site. Sometimes hours later, the dive has not yet begun.

There's a better way: Make a boat your home. Nearly every diving destination in the Caribbean, and an increasing number in other oceans, now offer well-run, though sometimes expensive, shipboard diving and snorkeling vacations. These allow you to avoid overused sites, to reach reefs that day-trippers can only dream of, and to encounter the reef world in its pristine state.

To divers accustomed only to Atlantic reefs, the coral gardens of the Indian Ocean present a stunning new frontier.

THE INDIAN OCEAN: UNKNOWN GLORIES

To those accustomed to the large, often tightly packed islands of the southwest Atlantic, the first view of the world's other tropical oceans is often surprising—even stunning.

The Indian Ocean, one notices immediately, is a vast expanse of blue-green water, speckled with tiny islands. Reaching the Maldives, the Seychelles, or other island groups requires hours upon hours of plane travel or a several-week-long boat trip from almost any starting point.

Even though it takes so long to get there, no snorkeler or diver turns down the opportunity to visit the Indian Ocean's island paradises, particularly the Maldives, which are the most "diver-friendly" of all Indian Ocean island reefs. Here you'll find some of the world's most spectacular, awe-inspiring, and adventurous diving, as well as some of the most fascinating and unspoiled human cultures left on earth.

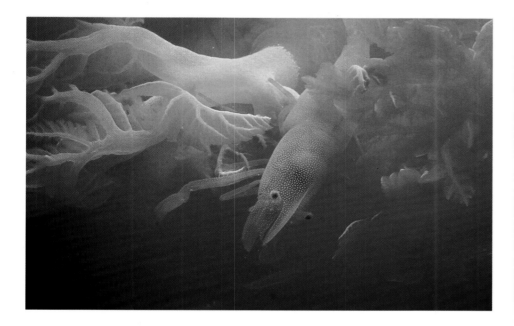

Of all the nudibranchs inhabiting the Indian Ocean, none is more bizarre or spectacular than the Spanish dancer, which can reach twelve inches (30 cm) in length.

Kenya

You don't have to island-hop to enjoy the pleasures of Indian Ocean snorkeling and diving. If you happen to be on an East African safari and would like to add some undersea wildlife to your list of game seen, Kenya offers snorkeling and diving on reefs located just offshore. But don't expect the spotless spectacle that any reef on the Maldives offers, because some of the Kenyan reefs have been adversely affected by onshore development.

Much fine and accessible snorkeling and diving remains, however, along Kenya's approximately three hundred miles (480 km) of reef, particularly during the dry seasons (July through September and December through March). In recent years, this country, which already contains one of the finest land national park systems in the world, has also begun to protect some of its marine riches. Thus far, Kenya has set aside Malindi and Watamu Marine National Parks, both of which are located near Malindi, an Arabic town on the northeast coast. Recently, Kenya has also named new marine parks near the Tanzanian border to the south and the Somalian border to the north, and plans to create several others are underway.

Most visitors, however, still make the beachside hotels near Malindi their homebase. For a first look at the reef inhabitants of this region, you don't even need to bring your gear. At low tide, you can walk from any of the white-sand beaches into water that is never more than thigh deep for as long as a mile (1.6 km), and end up on the reef crest itself.

Kenya's inshore reefs are a particular delight for the snorkeler: Shallow, brightly lit, and rich in both coral and other marine life, they could not be easier to explore. Here, as well as in deeper water, look out for the longnosed butterflyfish and rainbow redfins, as common here as on the Maldivian reefs, as well as a fascinating variety of triggerfish, including the Picasso, orange-striped, and ridiculously garish clown triggerfish.

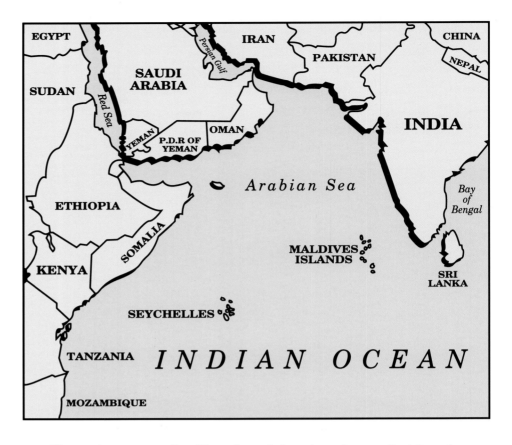

The water surrounding Kenya's reefs is not as clear as that found elsewhere in the Indo-Pacific. Therefore, reef-building corals, with their requirements for light, do not grow well in the deeper waters here. They are replaced instead by soft corals, gorgonians, and multicolored sponges, which add a softer edge to the reef environment.

Divers in these murky waters have reported that cardinalfish and other normally nocturnal fish are active during the day on Kenya's dark reefs. Sightings of such spectacular ocean denizens as giant sea turtles and whale sharks are also more common here than elsewhere.

Unfortunately, it may be advisable to visit Kenya's reefs soon, if at all. Recent reports say that increased forest clearing inland has led to substantially greater fresh-water runoff along many rivers. The runoff carries sediment and pollutants to the reef—a sure recipe for killing coral. (For more on the increasing threats to the world's reefs, see Chapter Five: A World Without Reefs?)

Maldives

If you've ever visited the Maldives, or spoken to someone who has, then you know that premier unknown reef destinations still exist. Located about five hundred miles (800 km) southwest of Sri Lanka, the Maldives comprise more than a thousand islands scattered over five hundred miles (800 km) of crystal blue ocean. Most of the islands are tiny palm-fringed specks on the water; fewer than a quarter are inhabited, and those that are have unpronounceable names like Thiladunmathi and Mulakatholhu.

The Maldives are home to some of the most perfectly formed atolls on earth. This is a volcano-riddled region, and doughnut-shaped and circular atolls are common here. Some of the world's largest atolls can be found in the Maldives, including some that are more than six miles (10 km) in diameter.

Underwater, almost anywhere you look, the Maldives present perhaps the richest reef spectacle on earth. Place yourself at any one of the countless gaps, called passes, in an atoll's reef, and you may find yourself overwhelmed by the number and variety of fish. It would be hard to imagine or invent a more spectacular sight. In water as shallow as three feet (1 m), stunned visitors will find themselves enveloped in clouds of fusiliers, fairy basslets, pennant butterflyfish, and other plankton feeders that hang in open water above the low-growing corals. But it is the occupants of the reefs themselves that seem nearly inconceivable to the visitor accustomed to Atlantic reefs.

At first glance, it seems that every butterflyfish on earth lives here. Brilliantly colored rainbow redfins, the longnosed butterflyfish (with its odd resemblance to an oilcan), and many others—always in pairs—dart amid the coral crags. Just as gaudy are the abundant angelfish, particularly the king and emperor angelfish and the orange-masked (or yellow-faced) angelfish, with its blue and yellow netting and its raccoonlike mask.

But don't stop with these showy reef representatives. Take the time to enjoy the boldly striped crinoids; the aggressive morays; the outrageously big and blocky humphead wrasses; the spiny sea urchins; and the two-foot- (.6-m-) long titan triggerfish, whose reef-crumbling hunts for food often attract large schools of opportunistic wrasses, parrotfish, and others.

These glass minnows are among the characteristic residents of Kenya's reefs.

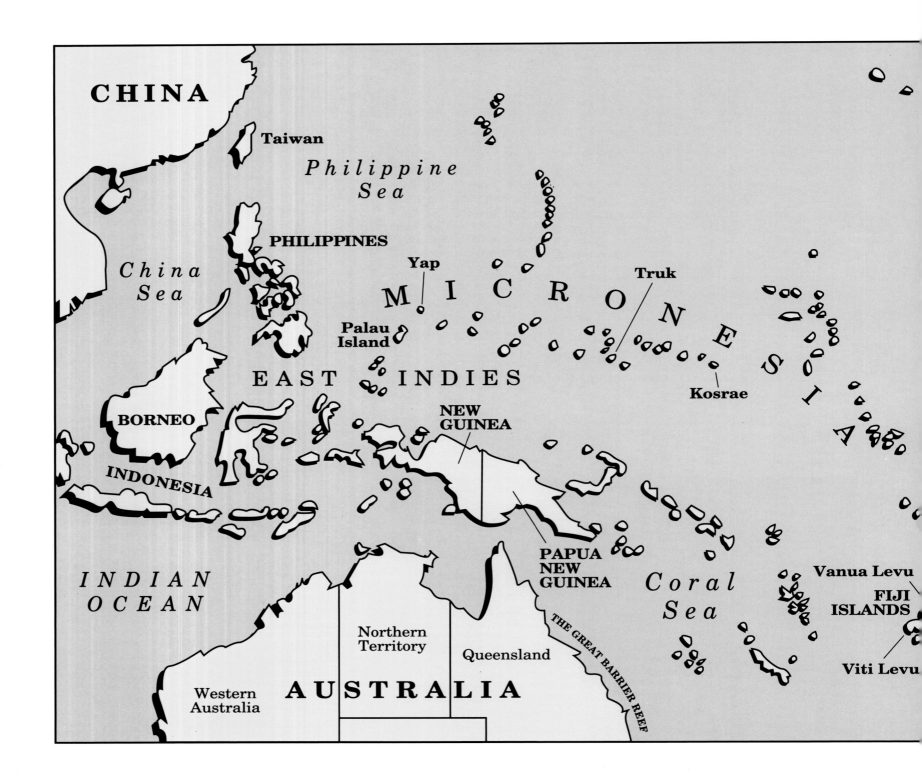

The map shows the Pacific Ocean region including CHINA, Taiwan, Philippine Sea, PHILIPPINES, China Sea, Yap, Palau Island, MICRONESIA, Truk, Kosrae, EAST INDIES, BORNEO, INDONESIA, NEW GUINEA, PAPUA NEW GUINEA, INDIAN OCEAN, Northern Territory, Queensland, Western Australia, AUSTRALIA, THE GREAT BARRIER REEF, Coral Sea, Vanua Levu, FIJI ISLANDS, Viti Levu.

THE PACIFIC OCEAN: A SCATTERING OF ISLANDS

If you thought that the Indian Ocean was a vast, featureless blue-green expanse, wait until you get a look at the Pacific. How empty is this gigantic ocean? The airplane flight from Los Angeles to Sydney, Australia, takes sixteen hours—almost every minute of which is over the Pacific.

Yet even the emptiest oceans contain scatterings of islands, and those located in the Pacific are both among the world's most plentiful (the Philippines alone contains more than seven thousand islands), and among the most beautiful. They can also boast some of the world's grandest and richest reefs. Some are famous, none more so than the Great Barrier Reef. Others, such as Yap and Palau, are virtually unknown outside of diving circles. Every one of them will richly reward the visitor.

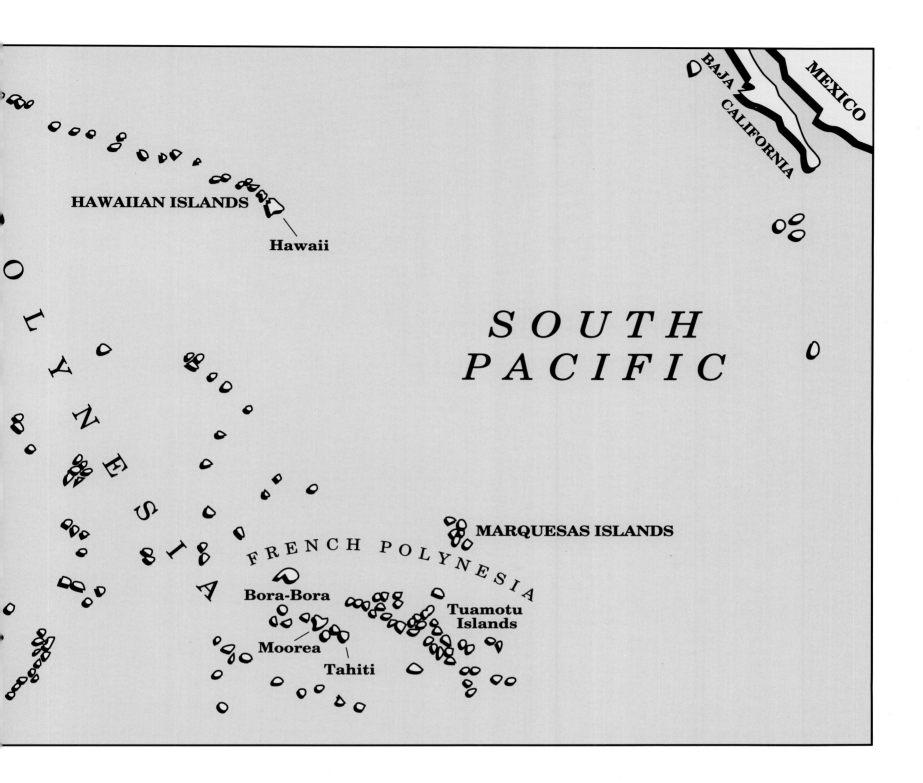

Australia: The Great Barrier Reef

The Great Barrier Reef is one of the world's most famous natural glories. Even for those who have spent a lifetime exploring this vast reef, its breadth and variety remain almost impossible to comprehend.

The Great Barrier Reef lies within the tropical Coral Sea, bordered on the west by the Australian coast and on the east by Vanuatu, New Caledonia, and other South Pacific islands. Beginning off the shore of south-central Queensland, this magnificent living structure twists and turns northward for an extraordinary 1,200 miles (2,000 kilometers), culminating in the Torres Strait, located between the top of Australia and southern Papua New Guinea. Overall, the reef covers an astounding 90,000 square miles (230,000 km), an area nearly the size of the state of Oregon.

Within this remarkable expanse lie more than 2,500 discrete reefs, including reefs fringing the Australian coast and many continental islands,

Within the almost unimaginable expanse of the Great Barrier Reef lies Heron Island and hundreds of other islands, each fringed by its own reefs.

patch reefs, lagoons, and cays, as well as more than 300 coral islands. Some of these reefs and islands lie in shallow water just off the Australian coast, while others skirt the edge of the continental shelf nearly 200 miles (320 km) offshore.

The abundance and diversity of life on the reef are as impressive as the size of the reef itself. Scientists estimate, and any diver can confirm, that a single acre (.4 ha) of reef may be occupied by 100,000 individual fish of 150 different species—an astounding variety of life. In addition, colorful crinoids, sea stars, and urchins; stealthy cuttlefish and octopuses; brightly banded shrimp; and the diverse and varied coral itself all contribute to the extraordinary richness of the Great Barrier Reef.

Yet, that doesn't mean that every spot on the reef is as exciting as any other. Many of the inshore reefs, in fact, can be surprisingly barren, with turbid water limiting visibility to fifty feet (15 m) or less. Elsewhere, shallow water and varying tides often limit reef growth, leaving the bleached skeletons of dead corals interspersed only occasionally with living coral heads.

In fact, many divers are disappointed by their first encounter with the Great Barrier Reef. To avoid disappointment, it's important to pick those spots that best suit your experience and desires. While most snorkelers (and many divers) will be thrilled by the coral located near the region's most famous island resorts, experienced divers may want to seek more remote sites located on the outer reef—or even more distant Coral Sea reefs. The following sections are a selection of the best locations, for both the neophyte and the professional diver, in roughly south-to-north geographical order.

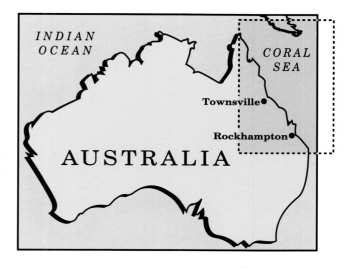

Keep in mind, though, that much of the best diving, and even some fine snorkeling, is found far from any of the following islands. For trips to the rich, undisturbed outer reef, you may have to join a charter live-aboard boat leaving from Townsville, Cairns, Port Douglas, or one of the other cities scattered along the Queensland coast.

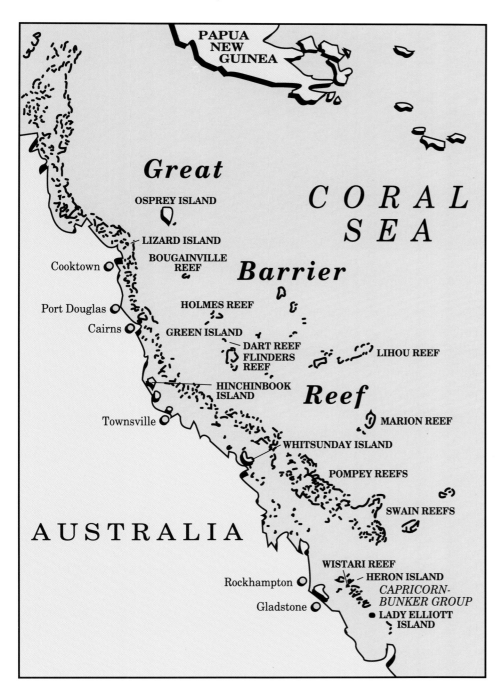

Lady Elliot Island

Located at the southernmost border of the Great Barrier Reef Marine Park, Lady Elliot Island is a forty-two-acre (17-ha) coral cay (an island actually composed of old coral), ringed by beautiful white sand, warm shallow water, and beautiful fringing reefs. Here divers and snorkelers often come upon some of the region's most spectacular marine denizens: manta rays, reef sharks (which are virtually harmless), and sea turtles.

The massive potato cod, actually a 250-pound (113-kg) grouper, is the most famous resident of the Great Barrier Reef's Cod Hole.

Heron Island

Set amid the islands of the Capricorn-Bunker Group, just north of Lady Elliot Island, Heron Island is one of the best known of all of Australia's reef resorts. Like Lady Elliot, Heron is a coral cay, exposed by the passage of time and changes in sea level. As a result, the thirty-five acres (14 ha) of reef surrounding the island are easily accessible to divers and snorkelers.

At such sites as the Bommies (a pair of enormous coral heads), Gorgonia Hole, and Blue Holes, visitors can admire a wide variety of typical Great Barrier Reef inhabitants, including barramundi cod, coral trout, parrotfish, and octopuses.

Swain and Pompey Reefs

Far more remote and not as well known as Heron Island, this 1,400-mile- (2,300-km-) long, and sometimes 200-mile- (320-km-) wide, stretch of reef contains some of the Great Barrier Reef's most spectacular coral formations. Heavy currents rushing through intricate coral channels make for challenging diving for these reefs' few visitors. This is a perfect destination for the expert diver on a live-aboard charter boat.

Townsville

Townsville isn't an island, but it is the jumping-off point to the beautiful, protected Green, Hinchinbook, and Lizard islands. It's also the best place to go if you want to reach one of the most dramatic dive sites on the whole barrier reef: the wreck of the *Yongala*. This coral-encrusted hull serves as a magnet for an awe-inspiring assemblage of the Great Barrier Reef's largest inhabitants. Sea turtles, potato cods and other huge groupers, sharks, rays, and large schooling snappers are almost guaranteed here, in numbers that defy comparison anywhere else on the reef.

In addition to these charms, Townsville is host to what may be the largest living "captive" reef on earth, the most impressive feature of its waterfront aquarium. Although a visitor may feel that such an exhibit would be more exciting in a cold-weather, reefless city like New York or London than on the edge of the Great Barrier Reef itself, Townsville's aquarium will give you a fine introduction to the sights that await you in the wild.

Green Island

Like Heron Island, Green Island is a coral cay with a resort built atop it. An easy twenty-five-mile (40-km) hop from the city of Cairns, this thirty-acre (12-ha) island features a theater, an underwater observatory for nonsnorkelers and nondivers, and many nearby reefs.

Unfortunately, a scourge of crown-of-thorns starfish has in recent years destroyed much of Green Island's most beautiful reefs. Other nearby reefs remain comparatively unaffected, however, and are still worth a visit, especially for those who desire comfortable resort living along with their reef explorations. (For more on the depredations of the crown-of-thorns starfish, see Chapter Five, page 115.)

The reefs surrounding Lizard Island are beautiful even from the air.

Lizard Island

Northernmost of the Great Barrier Reef's resorts, Lizard Island offers some of the region's best diving and snorkeling. Featuring rain forests, palm forests, giant (but harmless) monitor lizards, and twenty-four beaches fringed by coral, Lizard Island is also one of the quietest and least disturbed of all of Australia's island resorts. You shouldn't miss Cormorant Pass on Number 10 Ribbon Reef, which many experts consider to be the single best dive anywhere on the Great Barrier Reef's entire 1,200-mile (2,000-km) expanse.

In addition to spectacular coral scenery, visitors to Baja California can also view magnificent gray whales.

Baja California

You won't find towering coral spires in the waters off this arid peninsula in western Mexico. But divers jumping off from Los Cabos, set at the end of the peninsula, are still in for a treat. Baja California is home to dramatic underwater scenery with plunging abyssal canyons, occasional growths of gorgonians and hard corals, and spectacular reef life.

At such sites as Cabo Pulmo, The Point, and Conch Reef, visitors can also go searching for big game: manta rays leaping from the surf and splashing down with a sound like a thunderclap; eagle rays, which are almost as spectacular; whale sharks; and even humpback and gray whales.

Fiji

Almost everyone has a mental image of Fiji: an island boasting endless sand beaches fringed with palm trees, clear, warm ocean stretching to the horizon, and friendly, welcoming inhabitants. Actually, that's a pretty accurate picture, with just one major exception: Fiji isn't a single island, but hundreds of different islands, many of which remain uninhabited.

This is another location that could easily occupy years of diving time. To start, it's best to consider only the two largest islands, Viti Levu and Vanua Levu (which together harbor nearly the entire Fiji population), as well as those smaller islands within an easy hop of the two main ones.

Easily the most famous of all Fijian reefs is Great Astrolabe Reef, a tremendous set of ramparts and precipices, some plunging more than a mile (1.6 km) beneath the surface. These colossal walls, often coated by brilliant soft corals and gorgonians, are rent by fissures and chasms that grant fascinating exploration possibilities to the diver.

French Polynesia

Another far-flung group of islands united under a single name, French Polynesia includes such gorgeous islands as Tahiti, Moorea, and Bora-Bora; the Marquesas; and the spectacular Tuamotu Archipelago.

Due to storms, fresh-water runoff from island mountains, and unknown other factors, the coral reefs of French Polynesia are not quite as spectacular as the treasures found above water. Perhaps the best diving is found off the atoll Rangiroa, in the Tuamotu Archipelago, whose huge passes are frequented by abundant reef fish, as well as a large population of sharks.

V isiting the islands of French Polynesia, including this coral lagoon off Moorea, is like entering a world made of coral.

Hawaii

Few travelers visit Hawaii for its coral reefs, because the archipelago's location, the prevailing winds, and cold currents have severely limited the coral growth. Instead visitors go for its extraordinary beaches, its nightlife, and its blue water, which possesses a rich, warm color unlike that found anywhere else.

But many visitors may want to do some snorkeling or diving. You can still have a wonderful time off the comparatively undisturbed islands of Kauai and Lanai, drifting among lava tubes and ramparts that are often festooned with trees of stunning black coral. The marine life is surprisingly rich, with butterflyfish (including schools of lemon and smaller numbers of golden-slashed and four-spot butterflyfish), angelfish, Achilles tangs, and others.

Micronesia

You would be hard pressed to dive at every island in Micronesia. This island nation contains a stunning 2,100 small-to-tiny islands, covering an area nearly as large as the United States.

But if that seems like too large a task, then you can concentrate fruitfully on four areas within the great sprawl of Micronesia: the comparatively well-known Palau, Truk, and Yap, and the upstart newcomer Kosrae. Each provides its own unique diving thrills, echoes of history, the best wreck diving on earth, and unparalleled reef spectacles.

The Blue Hole of Palau (below) possesses an otherworldly beauty found on no other reef on earth.

Kosrae

If you're planning to visit Kosrae, located on the eastern edge of Micronesia, you're in for one of the treats of your life. This lush, mountainous island is completely surrounded by unspoiled and often completely unexplored reefs.

At such dive sites as Bus Stop and Shark's Rendezvous, you'll swim among an unbelievably dense assemblage of hard and soft corals, a riot of reef invertebrates (ranging from confettilike crinoids and huge, fleshy anemones to whirling nudibranchs), and such Pacific treasures as sea turtles, dolphins, and countless reef fish.

Palau

These westernmost islands of Micronesia, located southwest of Guam, challenge expert divers willing to brave turbulence and strong currents in order to view giant coral ramparts brimming with gaudy fish. Once again, be prepared for specialized diving requirements, and you'll have the ride of your life.

Palau's most famous dive spot—one of the most spectacular on earth—is the Blue Hole, an open cavern in the reef at 110 feet (33 m) below the surface. Enter the cavern, look up, and you'll be awed by a quartet of vertical shafts descending through ancient coral from the open ocean far above. These are the blue holes, which on bright days carry beams of sunlight flashing down into the dark cavern, creating a natural cathedral of almost incomprehensible beauty.

Truk

Truk is, without a doubt, the most famous of all Pacific islands, but this is not for any reason having to do with its beautiful reefs. Instead, this small, peaceful island gained its everlasting notoriety for its role in World War II, when it served as one of the most important bases of the Japanese navy.

In February, 1944, Allied warplanes sank more than sixty Japanese freighters, submarines, and other ships. Today, signs of the battle are still easy to see, but none more so than the wrecks that still litter Truk Lagoon. Hover in clear, calm water over the massive *Fujikawa Maru* or any of the other wrecks, and you'll receive a sobering reminder of the war. Over the past half-century, Truk Lagoon's wrecks have become magnificent artificial reefs, home to stony corals, gorgonians, and brilliantly colored sponges and soft corals. With the corals have come an abundance of reef fish, seeming both fragile and insubstantial amid the crumbling metal of Truk's ghostly hulls.

The ghostly hull of the *Fujikawa Maru* in Truk Lagoon has become home to a thriving assortment of reef denizens.

Yap

Northeast of Palau lie the Yap islands, perhaps the least known of Micronesia's premiere dive destinations. This is a coral paradise of four islands surrounded by forty-five miles (72 km) of dramatic, little-explored barrier reef, with water so clear that visibility can approach two hundred feet (60 m).

Drift along the vertical wall of Gilmaan Tip, and you'll view a spectacular array of gorgonians and soft corals, small reef fish, and large, ocean-going creatures, including tuna, jacks, and even sailfish. Cave enthusiasts won't want to miss Yap Caverns, a network of crumbling channels and caves that delves deep into the reef. And one of the best places in the world to view manta rays is also here: Manta Ridge, which often features as many as twenty of the tremendous creatures.

You'd be foolish to travel all the way to Micronesia without also taking some time to explore some of the islands' other treasures. Make sure to visit the gorgeous tropical forests to spot some of their rare and colorful birds and to learn about the fascinating ancient, and at times remarkably undisturbed, human cultures—which still maintain a strong sense of traditional South Pacific life.

Papua New Guinea

North of Australia and south of Micronesia lies the enormous, mountainous island of New Guinea, which contains some of the most remote wilderness and unspoiled primitive cultures left on earth. Covering the eastern half of the island is an independent nation named Papua New Guinea, which also boasts some fine diving and snorkeling opportunities.

Lying off the northeast coast of Papua New Guinea are miles of reefs. Within an hour's boat trip from the coastal town of Madang, you can explore reefs bursting with multicolored crinoids, butterflyfish and other reef fish, and even abundant sea snakes—a simultaneously exciting and sobering sight. Dive boats will take you to even more remote reefs fringing countless tiny islands, many of which were created by still-active volcanoes. (Note the onomatopoetic names given to two of these volcanic islands: Bam and Karkar!)

Birds of Paradise

What's even more beautiful than a clown triggerfish, a Spanish dancer nudibranch, or a school of butterflyfish: any of two dozen different birds of paradise. Native only to New Guinea and adjacent Australia, these gorgeous and bizarre birds, with their dramatic, diaphanous plumes and plush blue, crimson, and lemon feathers, were once thought to be messengers from heaven. Take the time to visit Papua New Guinea's southern highlands, and you'll have a good chance to see the spectacular mating displays (which sometimes involve the male bird's hanging upside-down from a branch, emitting a sound like an air-raid siren), of several different species.

Philippines

Nowhere on earth is the battle between conservation and exploitation more apparent, and more desperate, than in the approximately seven thousand islands that make up the Philippines—including their beautiful coral reefs. Visitors to many reefs report that evidence of dynamiting is common, despite laws passed to control the practice. Dynamiting not only kills a reef's fish (which then float to the surface, and are easily "harvested" by fishermen), but it also kills the reef itself.

To combat these dire developments, the Philippine government is making efforts to further protect its remaining reefs, many of which are outstandingly beautiful. One such protected reef is Apo Reef, which has spectacular assemblages of large anemones, complete with one of the world's densest populations of clownfish, as well as such dramatic creatures as manta rays and cuttlefish.

While the surrounding land may appear to be a barren desert, the reefs of the Red Sea contain dozens of fish and other reef denizens found nowhere else.

RED SEA: THE DESERT REEFS

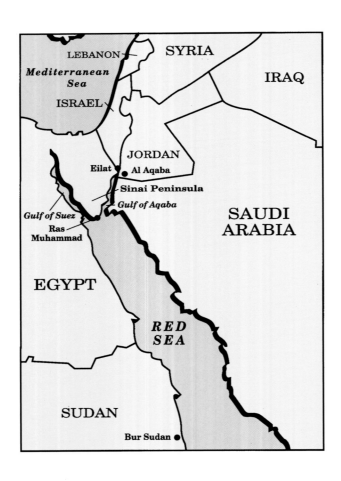

No coral reefs on earth remain less visited, and more yearned for, than those found in the Red Sea. For those willing to brave the harsh climate and political upheavals of the lands that surround them, the reefs that lie off Sudan, Jordan, Israel, and elsewhere in the region provide rich rewards.

The Red Sea, squeezed on all sides by the rocky, blistering deserts of North Africa and the Middle East, sits atop a tremendous abyss, a huge gap between tectonic plates that plunges over ten thousand feet (3,000 m) to the sea floor. As a result, the Red Sea's fringing reefs tend to be narrow, tightly packed, and densely populated, with many species of coral competing intensely for the limited space in the brightly lit shallows.

Yet these narrow reefs harbor an incredible number and diversity of marine animals, more than a quarter of which are found nowhere else on earth. Here thrive endemic angelfish, damselfish, butterflyfish, and others, often in numbers that equal or exceed those found on any Pacific reef.

During the past decade, Red Sea dive resorts have sprung up to provide access to the reefs off Eilat, Israel; Aqaba, Jordan; Sharm-el-Sheikh, in the Sinai Peninsula; and Port Sudan, Sudan. But the finest—and most easily accessible—of all the Red Sea's reefs is located at the very tip of the Sinai Peninsula, where the peninsula divides into the Gulf of Aqaba and the Gulf of Suez. This is Ras Muhammad, whose name has become a virtual mantra among daydreaming reef enthusiasts.

The walls and precipices of the Red Sea reefs, home to an amazing abundance of fish, are among these reefs' most distinctive features.

Ras Muhammad

Divers love Ras Muhammad's multicolored hard corals and brilliant gorgonians and soft corals. They are challenged by its precipitous slopes, its crags and ledges, and its mysterious, abyssal deeps. They are thrilled by its endlessly changing pageant of life: tiny cleaner wrasses, stunning orange-tailed butterflyfish, glorious emperor angelfish, and monstrous humphead wrasses, which can reach seven feet (2 m) in length. They love its morays, copper sweepers, triggerfish, tangs, parrotfish, and others, which provide an unparalleled reef spectacle.

But most of all, divers at Ras Muhammad are drawn by its big game: the spectacular open-ocean fish that congregate there, cruising the deep blue waters that lie just beyond the reefs. Here you can easily find enormous schools of barracudas, snappers, and jacks. Search a little harder, and you may be blessed by the pulse-quickening sight of large sharks, including the feared white-tip and hammerhead sharks.

CHAPTER FIVE:

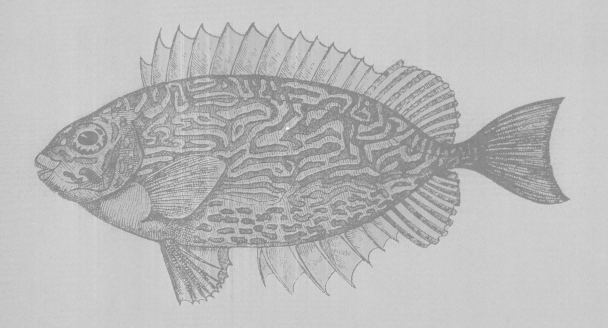

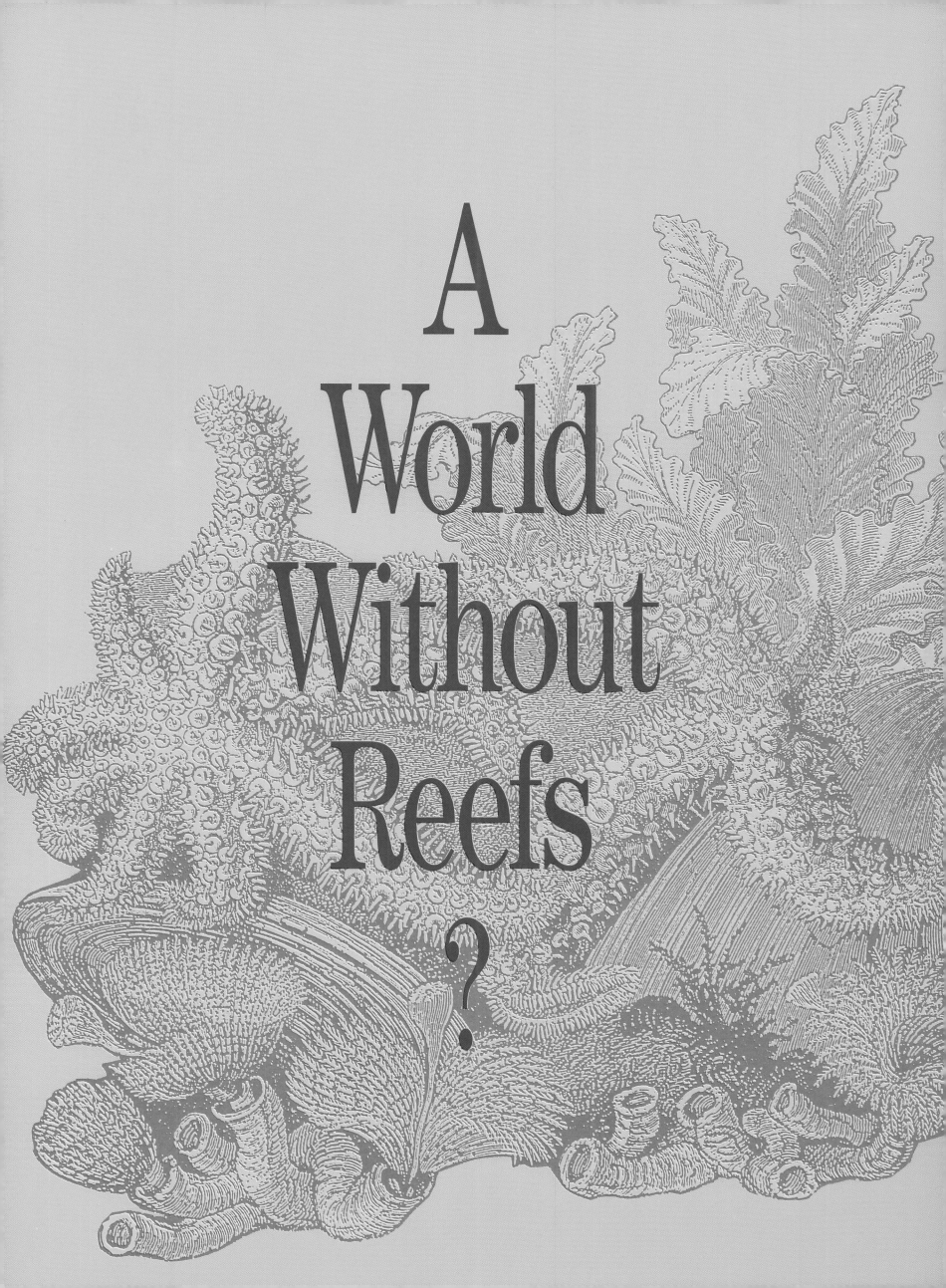

A
World
Without
Reefs
?

GREAT CORAL REEFS

ever before have the world's coral reefs been more accessible. Today, an ambitious diver can explore the finest reefs of the Caribbean, hop a jet to the magnificent coral caverns of the Maldives, jump over to the Coral Sea for a few days on a live-aboard boat cruising the outer Great Barrier Reef, check out Papua New Guinea's volcanic seamounts, take a dip among the hammerhead sharks at Ras Muhammad, and be home in less than a month. It's been done, and will be done again.

But if you want to be one of the people who does it, you'd better hurry up. An increasing number of reports from the reefs are leading scientists, divers, and other coral enthusiasts to a single frightening conclusion: The world's coral reefs, and the animals that inhabit them, are dying.

Far left: Overpopulation and overuse are helping to spell doom for many of Florida's most vulnerable reefs. Below: While corals are adaptable (these are growing on an old pier on Bonaire), they are also vulnerable to a host of threats.

The signs of the reefs' demise are becoming increasingly obvious, on reefs from the most heavily visited parks off the Florida Keys to the remotest atolls of the South Pacific. In just the past decade, many once-pristine reefs have been reduced to patches of lifeless rubble. Even more frightening, the trained eyes of scientists can see the signs of steady deterioration even on reefs that the rest of us would think completely healthy.

Recognizing the ongoing and ever-increasing destruction of the world's reefs, researchers have now begun to identify many of the factors causing the death of this irreplaceable natural wonder. The following section describes the various existing threats to the reefs, and then describes what scientists, governments, and others are doing—and should be doing—to safeguard what remains of one of the world's most spectacular ecosystems.

A single fish trap can decimate the populations of fish for acres of reef.

FISHING

Fishing wouldn't seem to have a direct impact on the health of the reef. But it does have a powerful impact, one which can destroy the fragile structure of life on the reef.

Coral reefs have long served as prime sources of food for the countries whose coastlines they fringe. On many unprotected reefs, spear-, line-, and net-fishing quickly decimate populations of groupers and other large, and tasty, predators. It's crucial to remember that the health of the reef depends on a complex, and not fully understood, interrelationship among hundreds of different species of coral, fish, and other animals. This interrelationship has been evolving over millions of years, and reefs do not have the capacity to adjust quickly to sudden population shifts. Therefore, the disappearance of even a single fish species can have a dramatic effect on the entire reef ecosystem.

For example, when humans cause the local extinction of one species of grouper, it encourages a population boom among the damselfish that are the grouper's usual prey. The skyrocketing population of damselfish will compete for food and safe shelter with less aggressive species, such as wrasses. As a result, the wrasse population will crash, depriving parrotfish and other larger species of the "cleaner" fish they need to stay healthy. The declining populations of these fish will, in turn, affect still others, a ripple effect that ultimately causes irreparable damage to the reef system itself.

Fish traps, widely employed near Caribbean and other reefs, have a more insidious effect on reef life. These barrel-shaped wooden traps, attached by a rope to a floating buoy, are dropped from a fishing boat and rest on the sandy bottom near the reef; they're a common sight near many frequently visited dive sites. Baited with dead fish, fish traps attract groupers and other food fish, which enter the traps through a narrow opening in one side and are then unable to escape. After a few days, the fishermen then pull up the trap, remove the catch, rebait the trap, and send it back to the bottom.

Frequently, however, the line connecting these traps to the floating buoy frays and parts, and the traps are lost to their owners. But this doesn't mean they stop functioning on the bottom. Predators continue to enter the trap, eat the bait, and eventually die from hunger. Their rotting corpses attract other predators, which themselves are then doomed to starvation. The trap becomes a virtual vacuum cleaner, sucking up and destroying countless fish before it finally rots away itself.

Other fishing techniques cause much more direct damage to the reef than do fish traps and spearfishing. Dynamiting of reefs indiscriminately kills fish, invertebrates, coral—the entire reef—leaving behind merely rubble. Dead fish then float to the surface, where those desired for food are collected, and the rest are left to rot. The blasted areas on the reef seem to remain barren and lifeless for years, perhaps decades.

When dynamite isn't available, teams of swimmers may carry rocks attached to long ropes. Forming a line, they drop the rocks onto the reef below and then swim forward, pounding the reef and frightening the fish into preset nets. Not only are the fish killed, including inedible "trash" species, but the coral itself is pounded into fragments.

All of these fishing techniques remain widespread on the world's reefs, particularly on those within the territory of developing countries. But many countries have begun to recognize the fragility, beauty, and value (through sustainable harvesting or tourism) of their reefs, and to control the formerly unfettered plundering. The Philippines, for example, has outlawed dynamiting of reefs. Nearly 100 percent of the Great Barrier Reef is protected from spearfishing or fish-trapping, as are certain reefs surrounding islands in the Caribbean and Indo-Pacific regions. Each year, forward-thinking countries like the Maldives, Kenya, Belize, and many others establish new marine parks.

LACK OF PROTECTION

But even when a country claims to be protecting its reefs, through a marine park or otherwise, protection may be insufficient or totally lacking. The Philippines, Jordan, Kenya, and other poor or strife-ridden countries simply cannot afford to provide the boats needed to patrol the protected areas or the guards to do the patrolling.

As a result, divers and others visiting many marine parks report the presence, often brazenly obvious, of fishing boats directly above supposedly protected reefs, as well as the blasted rubble that shows where covert dynamiters have been at work. Only through financial help from the United States and other wealthy countries, and through increased diligence on the part of the countries containing these parks, can promised preservation be translated into real protection.

COLLECTING

Professional collectors and tourists alike wreak havoc on the fragile reef ecosystem.

During the past year, you've probably been in a room or with a person decorated with the dead remains of a resident of the coral reef. It may have been a hunk of gleaming black or bleached-white coral, now used as a paperweight or a necklace or a pair of earrings. Perhaps it was a dried corpse of a coral-reef fish, most likely a grotesquely inflated, lacquered porcupinefish with staring glass eyes.

People who own such objects are participating in an industry that contributes directly to the defilement of reef ecosystems throughout the world. With the rise in popularity of diving and snorkeling, such collecting has become an ever-increasing, undeniable threat to the long-term health of coral reefs.

Perhaps the best-known example of the destructive powers of collecting is the plight of black coral. In previous decades, this stunningly beautiful, uncommon deep-water coral was highly desired for jewelry. Coral-hunters, seeking to supply the intense demand, attacked reefs such as the magnificent Palancar off Cozumel, Mexico. They left behind a decimated reef that despite years of protection, still looks more like a battlefield than a healthy coral garden.

The inexplicable demand for lacquered porcupinefish appears to have caused just as drastic consequences in the unique and vulnerable Red Sea reefs. Here, the disappearance of one species of porcupinefish, *Diodon hystrix*, may have led to a population explosion of sea urchins. Though the urchins did not directly eat the coral, they killed the fragile polyps while hunting for algae, their preferred food. Enormous areas of reef were destroyed by this out-of-control influx of urchins.

Another serious threat to the reefs is the hobby of keeping a live saltwater aquarium full of clownfish, damselfish, banded shrimp, and other gorgeous reef creatures. Most people are not aware that this hobby may be even more harmful to the reef than tearing it apart for coral. Almost every captive reef fish is wild-caught; commercial breeding of these species has not yet proven to be successful, except in very few cases. Researchers simply can't duplicate in captivity the complex conditions that allow reef fish to breed in the wild.

Stunning black coral trees have long caught the eye of collectors, resulting in the destruction of Palancar Reef and many others.

In addition, some of the same factors that make captive breeding so difficult also present challenges to the capturer. Reef fish have had millions of years to evolve defense mechanisms to escape predators, making capturing them a difficult and time-consuming process. In the past, collectors have risen to the challenge by stunning the fish on a reef with poison, such as cyanide, or even by harpooning them. One can only imagine how many individual fish died for each one that made it into an aquarium.

Even today, when such barbaric collecting techniques are less prevalent, mortality among captive fish is still high—even before they reach the pet store. These delicate creatures are designed for survival on the reef, not in a small holding tank aboard an airplane or a boat. As a result, the collector's only option is to capture as many of the fish as possible, even if it means removing every single one from the reef.

Governments, environmental organizations, and others have begun working to limit the destructive collecting of fish and coral. But this is one threat that individuals far from the reef can also battle, by refusing to buy jewelry or other products made of coral, by shunning stuffed fish, and by telling others to do the same. People who insist on keeping a saltwater aquarium should, at the very least, be discerning about the fish they keep and try to stick with less expensive, more common species. It is helpful to keep in mind that in general, the more expensive the fish and the rarer it is in the wild, the more difficult it was to capture and keep alive, and the more likely it is that its removal did serious damage to the reef's web of life.

TOURISM

A single misstep by a careless diver can kill a coral head that may have taken centuries to grow.

No one disputes that the burgeoning interest in snorkeling and diving has helped draw attention to the need to protect the world's reefs. Unfortunately, the more people that visit a reef, the more likely it is that a few will inflict damage on the very coral they've come to admire.

Some of the damage is a direct result of the numbers of tourists. Out-of-control or careless divers may crash into the reef, breaking off and killing fragile coral heads, gorgonians, or soft corals. Visitors to Key Largo and other heavily visited reefs will immediately notice the ugly brown dead spots on nearly every brain coral, evidence of the destruction that a swim fin, momentarily rested atop the seemingly impervious coral, can do.

Boats ferrying divers and snorkelers to pristine reefs can do even more damage. Pollution from boat engines and sewage is an increasing problem,

as is jettisoned trash ranging from metal cans to styrofoam cups. Where permanent moorings do not exist, boats must drop anchor on top of the reef. A several-hundred-pound metal weight can wreak as much havoc on a reef as a wrecking ball.

Other side effects of tourism begin onshore. The more popular the reef, the more likely that nearby coasts will become the site of resorts, dive shops, and other developments. These buildings, and the people that occupy them, generate waste water and other pollution, which can affect reefs for miles around.

Many popular dive sites have responded to these threats by installing permanent moorings, limiting the number of visitors, and hiring guides to keep a wary eye out for careless divers and snorkelers. Still, it seems that the completely untouched, pristine reef may soon be only a lovely memory.

ACCIDENTS

Even remote, unexploited, seldom-visited reefs aren't immune to the heavy footprint of human activity. Every oil spill in tropical waters (there are thousands each year, small and large) pollutes all of the reefs within miles. No one knows for sure how much of this pollution a reef can handle without dying.

In ancient times, hidden reefs were deeply feared by sailors; certain reefs claimed hundreds of ships attempting to navigate to shore. Today, ships still crash into nearly every coastal reef on earth, causing untold damage on impact and often spilling toxic substances directly onto the reef.

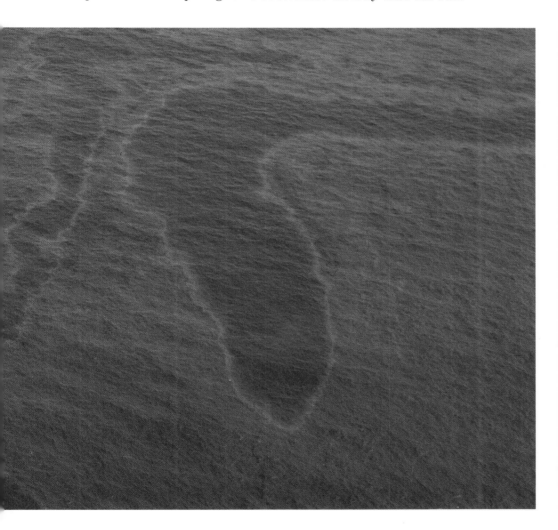

Oil spills, thousands of which occur every year, poison the reef and all of its inhabitants.

FRESH-WATER RUNOFF

The slightest change in salinity, water temperature, or visibility can mean the difference between healthy elkhorn coral (above, left), or coral that is dying (above, right). The crown-of-thorns starfish (far right) alone has destroyed sections of the Great Barrier Reef.

As we've seen, coral reefs are fragile and exacting ecosystems, requiring precise temperatures, salinity levels, and water clarity in order to thrive. As a result, any unnatural influx of fresh water will damage even the healthiest reef. Take a look at a reef ecosystem close to a mouth of a river, and you're likely to see stunted, unhealthy, algae-ridden coral. Even reefs far from river mouths can be damaged during floods, although the damage is rarely fatal.

Today, however, more and more coastal reefs are being destroyed by fresh-water runoff. The problem isn't that there's more fresh water in our streams and rivers than there used to be, but that far more of it is reaching the reefs. This problem is the result of deforestation, the removal of trees for farmland and other development. Undisturbed, tree-lined rivers are less likely to seriously overflow their banks, for thirsty trees drink much of the excess water that would otherwise flood. Trees are a crucial linchpin in the stability of the river environment.

In the past two decades, thoughtless, uncontrolled logging in Kenya, the Philippines, and many other countries has led to vastly increased runoff. This influx of fresh water has altered temperature and salinity levels, clogged miles of reef with silt and sediment, and carried chemical pesticides and other pollutants to formerly undisturbed reefs. The outcome, many scientists fear, will be the ongoing degradation of all reefs located anywhere near the coast.

CROWN-OF-THORNS STARFISH

Increasingly, visitors to the magnificent Great Barrier Reef are spotting large patches of reef that resemble a battlefield after the battle is over: scattered white skeletons of dead corals, interspersed with small fragments of living, but gravely damaged, coral.

The culprit in this onslaught is a spiky creature called the crown-of-thorns starfish, *Acanthaster planci*. The crown-of-thorns is a large, aggressive sea star, from twelve to fifteen inches (30 to 38 cm) across and with as many as twenty-three arms. It feeds on coral polyps, as it has for millions of years, but until the late 1960s the starfish existed in small enough numbers not to do any noticeable damage to the reef.

The past twenty years, however, have seen repeated population explosions of the crown-of-thorns, both on the Great Barrier Reef and elsewhere in the Indo-Pacific region. Thousands of the starfish descend on a section of reef, reducing huge expanses of reef to rubble, and then move on.

Scientists have long debated what causes the crown-of-thorns population explosions. Some believe that it's part of a natural boom-and-bust cycle, and that the affected reefs will recover. Others, though, fear that human interference with the reef, especially the unfettered shell-collecting of the triton, a beautiful mollusk that is the starfish's main predator, may be upsetting the natural balance and enabling the crown-of-thorns to do permanent damage.

GLOBAL WARMING

Will coral bleaching, the result of gradually increasing water temperatures, spell the end of the world's coral reefs?

Most of the threats discussed above occur on a local level, and therefore can be addressed and battled through local action. But the most serious threat to the continued health of coral reefs is occurring on a worldwide basis. It's the phenomenon known as global warming, and scientists fear that one of its effects, called coral bleaching, may result in the death of most or all reefs, in every ocean on earth.

As each year passes, the evidence that the earth's atmosphere is growing steadily warmer becomes clearer. Overall, worldwide temperatures in the 1980s were four degrees Fahrenheit higher than those of any other recorded decade. And 1990 was the warmest year ever recorded.

Many scientists attribute global warming to the "greenhouse effect," a condition where a variety of airborne pollutants trap heat, which otherwise would have leached into space, within the earth's atmosphere. The main culprit is carbon dioxide, produced when oil and other fuels are burned for energy. The problem is made even worse by the rampant deforestation occurring in the Amazon rain forests and other forests of the world. Trees take carbon dioxide out of the atmosphere during photosynthesis. With thousands of acres of forest being cleared each day, more and more carbon dioxide is left to clog the atmosphere.

As we've seen, overly warm water is one of the stresses that can kill a coral reef. While most reefs can tolerate brief periods of warmth, they are much more seriously affected by prolonged high temperatures, such as have occurred during the past decade. The corals react to these stresses by expelling their zooxanthellae. The loss of the microscopic algae turns the coral a pale, eerie white: the characteristic signs of coral bleaching. While most corals can survive an episode of bleaching, repeated episodes can fatigue the coral past the point of recovery.

Worldwide, bleaching has become an ever-increasing, ever-intensifying threat. More than 80 percent of the Atlantic's reefs have suffered from it since 1988, and researchers have also reported serious incidences of bleaching on the Great Barrier Reef, Hawaii, Fiji, and many other locations. While some of these reefs have recovered, others, already weakened, have fallen victim to disease or new episodes of bleaching. In many of the world's reefs, the ghostly, blasted battlefield may become an increasingly frequent sight.

CONCLUSION: WHAT WE CAN DO

Divers and snorkelers have a responsibility to the coral reefs whose beauty and mystery they so enjoy. Everyone with even the slightest interest in the future of the world's reefs must contribute to the intensifying effort to save the reefs.

On a personal level, be a careful and considerate visitor to the reef environment. Follow these rules, and you'll be helping your favorite reefs survive.

- Don't stand or lean on any patch of living reef—not even for an instant.
- Don't break off even a little piece of reef for a souvenir; that small fragment may have taken centuries to grow in that spot.
- Don't collect living shellfish or any other living creature.
- Don't buy any black-coral jewelry or anything else made from the reef or its inhabitants.
- Don't spearfish, even where it's allowed.
- Don't keep an aquarium containing reef denizens.
- Support organizations devoted to protecting or studying coral reefs.
- If you visit a marine park and don't like the way it's being treated, complain to the authorities.
- Fight rampant deforestation of the world's tropical forests. You'll be helping to save the rain forest (another of the world's most spectacular and fascinating environments), battling global warming, and reducing reef-killing runoff, all at the same time.
- Use energy efficiently. It's one personal way to combat global warming.

Good luck. See you on the reef.

PHOTOGRAPHY CREDITS

All photographs © Stephen Frink/Waterhouse unless otherwise indicated below.

© Rod & Kathy Canham/Waterhouse: pages 28, 42 bottom, 47 center right, 49 center left, 110, 115 bottom right

© Barbara Doernback/Waterhouse: page 47 bottom right

© Mike Goodwin/Waterhouse: page 44 bottom left

© William J. Harrigan/Waterhouse: page 112 center left

© Chris McLaughlin/Waterhouse: page 39 top

© Donna McLaughlin/Waterhouse: pages 41 bottom right, 44 center left

© Geri Murphy/Waterhouse: pages 53 bottom right, 95, 97, 98, 101

© Carl Roessler/Waterhouse: pages 16 left, 43 top left, 52 bottom, 69, 99

© Jerry Schnabel/Waterhouse: page 44 top right

© Marty Snyderman: page 96

© Marty Snyderman/Waterhouse: pages 39 bottom, 44 top left, 48 bottom left, 66, 72 bottom left

© Susan Lee Swygert/Waterhouse: pages 40 top left, 46 top left

All maps and illustrations © Scott MacNeill

BIBLIOGRAPHY

Faulkner, Douglas and Barry Fell. *Dwellers in the Sea*. New York: Reader's Digest Press, 1976.

Greenberg, Idaz and Jerry Greenberg. *Guide to Corals & Fishes of Florida, the Bahamas and the Caribbean*. Miami: Seahawk Press, 1977.

Holliday, Les. *Coral Reefs*. Morris Plains, N.J.: Tetra Press, 1989.

Nagelkerken, Wil. *Coral Reef Fishes of Aruba, Bonaire and Curaçao*. [Willemstad]: Island Territory of Curaçao, 1980.

Reader's Digest Visitors' Guide to the Great Barrier Reef. Sydney: Reader's Digest Press, 1988.

Roessler, Carl. *Coral Kingdoms*. New York: Harry N. Abrams, 1986.

Page numbers in italics refer to captions, illustrations, and sidebars.